For Your Delight

For Your Delight

*An Anthology for Children
of any Age*

Edited by
Ethel L. Fowler
Editor of *The Daffodil Book*

London
Faber and Faber Limited
24 Russell Square

First published, November 1924
Reprinted, 1925, 1927, 1929, 1931, 1934
Reset and reprinted, 1935
Reprinted 1939, 1942, 1944, 1945, 1946, 1947, 1949 and 1952.

Made and printed in Great Britain
by R. MacLehose & Co., Ltd.
The University Press, Anniesland, Glasgow

INDEX OF AUTHORS

Authors, their representatives, and Publishers, to whom the Compiler desires to make grateful acknowledgments for permission to use copyright poems, are named in parentheses after the Authors' names.

9

The Compiler has been unable to trace the source of 'The Crow', by Mrs. Alexander, and 'The All Alone Tree', by F. O'Neill Gallagher. She has ventured to include them and now makes due acknowledgment.

For Your Delight

I. ROUND THE YEAR

The crocus, while the days are dark,
   Unfolds its saffron sheen;
At April's touch, the crudest bark
   Discovers gems of green.

Then sleep the seasons, full of might;
   While slowly swells the pod
And rounds the peach, and in the night
   The mushroom bursts the sod.

The winter falls; the frozen rut
   Is bound with silver bars,
The snowdrift heaps against the hut
   And night is pierced with stars.

COVENTRY PATMORE

2. FEBRUARY

To-day I saw the catkins blow,
Altho' the hills are white with snow;

While throstles sang, 'The sun is good,'
They waved their banners in the wood.

They come to greet the lurking Spring
As messengers from Winter's King.

And thus they wave while Winter reigns,
While his cold grip still holds the plains.

Oh, tho' the hills are white with snow,
To-day I saw the catkins blow!

DOROTHY UNA RATCLIFFE

3. THE LITTLE YOUNG LAMBS

In the fold
On the wold
There were little young lambs,
An' the wind blew so cold
They laid lee o' their dams,
An' a shepherd old man
He leaned over the cotes,
An' a lilt he began
With a flutter of notes,
The little young lambs all among;
Oh, he piped 'em a derry down derry, he did,
Since they were so young.

An' they stirred
When they heard,
Did the little young lambs,
Then they hopped most absurd,
From a-lee of their dams,
An' they jumped and they skipped
With tip-toppetty skips,
As the little tune tripped
From the reed at the lips
Of the crinkled old man o' the wold,
As he piped 'em a merry down derry, he did,
Since he was so old.

For he blew
That he knew
Why the seasons went round,
An' why the green wheat grew
To his pipe's pretty sound;
An' why rain follows sun,
An' how sun follows rain,
An' how everything's done
To be started again,
Till the stars like ripe acorns shall fall;
An' he piped 'em his derry down derry, he did,
Along of it all.

PATRICK CHALMERS

4. FLOWER CHORUS

O such a commotion under the ground,
When March called 'Ho, there! ho!'
Such spreading of rootlets far and wide,
Such whisperings to and fro!
'Are you ready?' the Snowdrop asked,
' 'Tis time to start, you know.'
'Almost, my dear!' the Scilla replied,
'I'll follow as soon as you go.'
Then 'Ha! ha! ha!' a chorus came
Of laughter sweet and slow,
From millions of flowers under the ground,
Yes, millions beginning to grow.

'I'll promise my blossoms,' the Crocus said,
'When I hear the blackbird sing.'
And straight thereafter Narcissus cried,
'My silver and gold I'll bring.'

'And ere they are dulled,' another spoke,
    'The hyacinth bells shall ring.'
But the Violet only murmured 'I'm here,'
    And sweet grew the air of spring.
Then 'Ha! ha! ha!' a chorus came
    Of laughter sweet and low,
From millions of flowers under the ground,
    Yes, millions beginning to grow.

O the pretty brave things, thro' the coldest days
    Imprisoned in walls of brown,
They never lost heart tho' the blast shrieked loud,
    And the sleet and the hail came down;
But patiently each wrought her wonderful dress,
    Or fashioned her beautiful crown,
And now they are coming to lighten the world
    Still shadowed by winter's frown.
And well may they cheerily laugh 'Ha! ha!'
    In laughter sweet and low,
The millions of flowers under the ground,
    Yes, millions beginning to grow.

                            RALPH WALDO EMERSON

5. A MARCH DAY

The cock is crowing,
The stream is flowing,
The small birds twitter,
The lake doth glitter,
The green field sleeps in the sun;
The oldest and youngest
Are at work with the strongest;

14

The cattle are grazing,
Their heads never raising;
There are forty feeding like one!

Like an army defeated
The snow hath retreated,
And now doth fare ill
On the top of the bare hill;
The ploughboy is whooping-anon-anon;
There's joy in the mountains;
There's life in the fountains;
Small clouds are sailing ;
Blue sky prevailing;
The rain is over and gone!

WILLIAM WORDSWORTH

6. SPRING MORNING

Now the moisty wood discloses
Wrinkled leaves of primèroses,
While the birds, they flute and sing:
Build your nests, for here is Spring.

All about the open hills
Daisies shew their peasant frills,
Washed and white and newly spun
For a festival of sun.

Like a blossom from the sky,
Drops a yellow butterfly,
Dancing down the hedges grey
Snow-bestrewn till yesterday.

15

Squirrels skipping up the trees
Smell how Spring is in the breeze,
While the birds, they flute and sing:
Build your nests, for here is Spring.
FRANCES CORNFORD

7. FIRST SPRING MORNING

A CHILD'S POEM

Look! Look! the spring is come:
O feel the gentle air,
That wanders thro' the boughs to burst
The thick buds everywhere!
The birds are glad to see
The high unclouded sun:
Winter is fled away, they sing,
The gay time is begun.

Adown the meadows green
Let us go dance and play,
And look for violets in the lane,
And ramble far away
To gather primroses,
That in the woodland grow,
And hunt for oxslips, or if yet
The blades of bluebells show

There the old woodman gruff
Hath half the coppice cut,
And weaves the hurdles all day long
Beside his willow hut.

We'll steal on him, and then
Startle him, all with glee
Singing our song of winter fled
And summer soon to be.
ROBERT BRIDGES

8. APRIL—A FANTASY

Now April's fingers softly strip the jewels from
   her crown,
And on the bosom of the Earth she gently drops
   them down,
Then with a light caressing touch she draws a veil
   of green
Across Earth's breast, and 'neath its folds lie hid
   the gems unseen.

Anon she showers with lavish hand the gauds from
   out her hair;
Anon she smiles, anon she weeps, and weeping
   looks so fair;
And o'er the earth bright gold she casts, from
   bracelet and from chain,
And looses pearls and diamonds all in a silver rain.

Lo! from the folds of greenest film, where late 'twas
   cold and bare,
Gleam forth the pearl and diamond inset with
   sapphire rare,
And now the bosom of the Earth is deck'd with
   finest sheen,
And prinkt with gems of April's gift of treasures,
   nowise mean.

17   B

And blackbirds sing, and thrushes chant their
      orisons at morn,
To see how April's stripped herself the Mother to
      adorn;
They sing sweet songs of violets, the purple
      flowers of pain,
And whitest flowers of sacrifice that grow in Love's
      domain.

9. EASTER (EXTRACT)

I got me flowers to straw Thy way,
I got me boughs off many a tree;
But Thou wast up by break of day,
And brought'st Thy sweets along with Thee.

The sun arising in the East,
Though he gave light, and th'East perfume,
If they should offer to contest
With Thy arising, they presume.

Can there be any day but this,
Though many sun to shine endeavour?
We count three hundred, but we miss:
There is but one, and that one ever.

GEORGE HERBERT

10. OXFORDSHIRE CHILDREN'S MAY SONG

Spring is coming, spring is coming,
    Birdies, build your nest;
Weave together straw and feather,
    Doing each your best.

Spring is coming, spring is coming,
    Flowers are coming too:
Pansies, lilies, daffodillies,
    Now are coming through.

Spring is coming, spring is coming,
    All around is fair;
Shimmer and quiver on the river,
    Joy is everywhere.

We wish you a happy May.
                    COUNTRY RHYME

II. MAY DAY

Good morning, lords and ladies, it is the first of
    May;
We hope you'll view our garland, it is so sweet and
    gay.

The cuckoo sings in April, the cuckoo sings in
    May,
The cuckoo sings in June, in July she flies away.

The cuckoo drinks cold water to make her sing so
    clear.
And then she sings Cuckoo! Cuckoo! for three
    months in the year.

I love my little brother and sister every day
But I seem to love them better in the merry
    month of May.
                    COUNTRY RHYME

12. SONG ON MAY MORNING

Now the bright morning-star, Day's harbinger,
Comes dancing from the East, and leads with her
The flowery May, who from her green lap throws
The yellow cowslip and the pale primrose.
   Hail, bounteous May, that dost inspire
   Mirth, and youth, and warm desire!
   Woods and groves are of thy dressing;
   Hill and dale doth boast thy blessing.
Thus we salute thee with our early song,
And welcome thee, and wish thee long.

JOHN MILTON

13. SPRING

Spring, the sweet Spring, is the year's pleasant
   king;
Then blooms each thing, then maids dance in a
   ring,
Cold doth not sting, the pretty birds do sing:
Cuckoo, jug-jug, pu-we, to-witta-woo!

The palm and the may make country houses gay,
Lambs frisk and play, the shepherds pipe all day,
And we hear aye birds tune this merry lay:
Cuckoo, jug-jug, pu-we, to-witta-woo!

The fields breathe sweet, the daisies kiss our feet,
Young lovers meet, old wives a-sunning sit,
In every street these tunes our ears do greet:
Cuckoo, jug-jug, pu-we, to-witta-woo!
   Spring, the sweet Spring.

THOMAS NASH

14. THE WOOD OF FLOWERS

I went to the Wood of Flowers,
   (No one was with me)
I was there alone for hours;
   I was happy as could be
In the Wood of Flowers.

There was grass on the ground,
   There were buds on the tree,
And the wind had a sound
   Of such gaiety,
That I was as happy,
   As happy could be,
In the Wood of Flowers.

JAMES STEPHENS

15. THE DUMB SOLDIER

When the grass was closely mown,
Walking on the lawn alone,
In the turf a hole I found
And hid a soldier underground.

Spring and daisies came apace;
Grasses hid my hiding place;
Grasses run like a green sea
O'er the lawn up to my knee.

Under grass alone he lies,
Looking up with leaden eyes,
Scarlet coat and pointed gun,
To the stars and to the sun.

When the grass is ripe like grain,
When the scythe is stoned again,
When the lawn is shaven clear,
Then my hole shall reappear.

I shall find him, never fear,
I shall find my grenadier;
But for all that's gone and come
I shall find my soldier dumb.

He has lived, a little thing,
In the grassy woods of spring;
Done, if he could tell me true,
Just as I should like to do.

He has seen the starry hours
And the springing of the flowers;
And the fairy things that pass
In the forests of the grass.

In the silence he has heard
Talking bee and ladybird,
And the butterfly has flown
O'er him as he lay alone.

Not a word will he disclose,
Not a word of all he knows.
I must lay him on the shelf,
And make up the tale myself.

ROBERT LOUIS STEVENSON

16. BREAKFAST TIME

The sun is always in the sky
    Whenever I get out of bed,
And I often wonder why
    It's never late.—My sister said
She did not know who did the trick,
    And that she did not care a bit,
And I should eat my porridge quick.
    . . . I think it's mother wakens it.

JAMES STEPHENS

17. SUMMER SUN

Great is the sun, and wide he goes
Through empty heaven without repose;
And in the blue and glowing days
More thick than rain he showers his rays.

Though closer still the blinds we pull
To keep the shady parlour cool,
Yet he will find a chink or two
To slip his golden fingers through.

The dusty attic spider-clad
He, through the keyhole, maketh glad;
And through the broken edge of tiles
In to the laddered hayloft smiles.

Meantime his golden face around
He bares to all the garden ground,
And sheds a warm and glittering look
Among the ivy's inmost nook.

Above the hills, along the blue,
Round the bright air with footing true
To please the child, to paint the rose,
The gardener of the World, he goes.

ROBERT LOUIS STEVENSON

18. LAUGHING SONG

When the green woods laugh with the voice of joy,
And the dimpling stream runs laughing by;
When the air does laugh with our merry wit,
And the green hill laughs with the noise of it;

When the meadows laugh with lively green,
And the grasshopper laughs in the merry scene,
When Mary and Susan and Emily
With their sweet round mouths sing 'Ha, Ha, He!'

When the painted birds laugh in the shade,
Where our table with cherries and nuts is spread,
Come live, and be merry, and join with me,
To sing the sweet chorus of 'Ha, Ha, He!'

WILLIAM BLAKE

19. MINNIE AND MATTIE

Minnie and Mattie,
   And fat little May,
Out in the country,
   Spending a day.

Such a bright day,
   With the sun glowing,
And the trees half in leaf,
   And the grass growing.

24

Pinky white pigling
  Squeals through his snout,
Woolly white lambkin
  Frisks all about.

Cluck! cluck! the nursing hen
  Summons her folk,—
Ducklings all downy soft,
  Yellow as yolk.

Cluck! cluck! the mother hen
  Summons her chickens
To peck the dainty bits
  Found in her pickings.

Minnie and Mattie,
  And May carry posies,
Half of sweet violets,
  Half of primroses.

Give the sun time enough,
  Glowing and glowing,
He'll rouse the roses
  And bring them blowing.

Don't wait for roses
  Losing to-day,
O Minnie, Mattie
  And wise little May.

Violets and primroses,
  Blossom to-day
For Minnie and Mattie
  And fat little May.

CHRISTINA ROSSETTI

20. NEST EGGS

Birds all the sunny day
Flutter and quarrel
Here in the arbour-like
Tent of the laurel.

Here in the fork
The brown nest is seated;
Four little blue eggs
The mother keeps heated.

While we stand watching her,
Staring like gabies,
Safe in each egg are the
Bird's little babies.

Soon the frail eggs they shall
Chip, and upspringing
Make all the April woods
Merry with singing.

Younger than we are,
O children, and frailer,
Soon on the blue air they'll be,
Singer and sailor.

We, so much older,
Taller and stronger,
We shall look down on the
Birdies no longer.

They shall go flying,
With musical speeches
High overhead in the
Tops of the beeches.

26

In spite of our wisdom
And sensible talking,
We on our feet must go
Plodding and walking.

ROBERT LOUIS STEVENSON

21. THE DOVE'S SONG

Coo-pe-coo, coo-pe-coo,
  Me and my poor two,
Two sticks across, and a little bit of moss,
  And it will do, do, do.

22. THE DOVE SAYS COO

The dove says Coo, coo, what shall I do?
I can scarce maintain two.
Pooh pooh, says the wren, I have got ten
And keep them all like gentlemen!

23. THE BOY WITH THE LITTLE BARE TOES

He ran all down the meadow, that he did,
  The boy with the little bare toes.
The flowers they smelt so sweet, so sweet,
And the grass it felt so funny and wet
And the birds sang just like this—'chereep!'
  And the willow-trees stood in rows.
    'Ho! ho!'
Laughed the boy with the little bare toes.

27

Now the trees had no insides—how funny!
  Laughed the boy with the little bare toes.
And he put in his hand to find some money
Or honey—yes, that would be best—oh, best!
But what do you think he found, found, found?
Why, six little eggs all round, round, round,
And a mother-bird on the nest,
      Oh, yes!
The mother-bird on her nest.

He laughed, 'Ha! ha!' and he laughed, 'He! he!'
  The boy with the little bare toes.
But the little mother-bird got up from her place
And flew right into his face, ho! ho!
And pecked him on the nose, 'Oh! oh!'
  Yes, pecked him right on the nose.
      'Boo! Boo!'
Cried the boy with the little bare toes.

WILLIAM HARVEY

24. THE LARK AND THE ROOK

'Good-night, Sir Rook,' said a little lark,
'The daylight fades, it will soon be dark;
I've bathed my wings in the sun's last ray,
I've sung my hymn to the dying day;
So now I haste to my quiet nook
In yon dewy meadow; good-night, Sir Rook.'

'Good-night, poor Lark,' said his titled friend,
With a haughty toss, and a distant bend;
'I also go to my rest profound,
But not to sleep on the cold damp ground;
The fittest place for a bird like me
Is the topmost bough of yon tall pine-tree.

28

'I opened my eyes at peep of day,
And saw you taking your upward way.
Dreaming your fond romantic dreams,
An ugly speck in the sun's bright beams,
Soaring too high to be seen or heard,
And said to myself, What a foolish bird!

'I trod the park with a princely air,
I filled my crop with the richest fare;
I cawed all day, mid a lordly crew,
And I made more noise in the world than you.
The sun shone forth on my ebon wing,
I looked and wondered—good-night, poor thing.'

'Good-night, once more,' said the lark's sweet
        voice;
'I see no cause to repent my choice.
You build your nest in the lofty pine,
But is your slumber more soft than mine?
You make more noise in the world than I,
But whose is the sweetest minstrelsy?'

25. SEVEN TIMES ONE

There's no dew left on the daisies and clover,
    There's no rain left in heaven:
I have said my 'Seven Times' over and over,
    Seven times one are seven.

I am old, so old I can write a letter;
    My birthday lessons are done;
The lambs play always, they know no better;
    They are only one times one.

O moon! in the night I have seen you sailing
  And shining so round and low;
You were bright! ah, bright! but your light is
      failing—
  You are nothing now but a bow.

You moon, have you done something wrong in
      heaven
  That God has hidden your face?
I hope, if you have, you will soon be forgiven,
  And shine again in your place.

O velvet bee, you're a dusty fellow,
  You've powdered your legs with gold!
O brave marsh-marybuds, rich and yellow,
  Give me your money to hold!

O columbine, open your folded wrapper,
  Where two twin turtle-doves dwell!
O cuckoo-pint, toll me the purple clapper
  That hangs in your clear green bell.

And show me your nest, with the young ones in it;
  I will not steal them away;
I am old! You may trust me, linnet, linnet—
  I am seven times one to-day.

JEAN INGELOW

26. THE LITTLE RED LARK

The little red lark is shaking his wings,
  Straight from the breast of his love he springs;
Listen the lilt of the song he sings,
  All in the morning early, O.

The sea is rocking a cradle, hark!
To a hushing-song, and the fields are dark.
And would I were there with the little red lark,
  All in the morning early, O.

The beard of barley is old-man's grey,
All green and silver the new-mown hay.
The dew from his wings he has shaken away,
  All in the morning early, O.

The little red lark is high in the sky;
No eagle soars where the lark may fly,
Where are you going to, high, so high?
  All in the morning early, O.

His wings and feathers are sunrise red;
He hails the sun and his golden head;
'Good-morrow, sun, you are long abed,'
  All in the morning early, O.

I would I were where the little red lark,
Up in the dawn like a rose-red spark,
Sheds the day on the fields so dark,
  All in the morning early, O.

                              KATHARINE TYNAN

27. DAY'S BLACK STAR

Is it that small black star,
    Twinkling in broad daylight,
Upon the bosom of
    Yon cloud so white—
Is it that small black thing
Makes earth and all Heaven ring!

31

Sing, you black star; and soar
    Until, alas! too soon
You fall to earth in one
    Long singing swoon;
But you will rise again
To heaven, from this green plain.

Sing, sing, sweet star; though black,
    Your company's more bright
Than any star that shines
    With a white light;
Sing, Skylark, sing; and give
To me thy joy to live.

WILLIAM H. DAVIES

28. ONE BLACKBIRD

The stars must make an awful noise
In whirling round the sky;
Yet somehow I can't even hear
Their loudest song or sigh.

So it is wonderful to think
One blackbird can outsing
The voice of all the swarming stars
On any day in spring.

HAROLD MONRO

29. THE DOVE

I had a dove and the sweet dove died;
    And I have thought it died of grieving:
O, what could it grieve for? Its feet were tied,
    With a silken thread of my own hands' weaving;

Sweet little red feet! why should you die—
Why should you leave me, sweet bird! why?
   You liv'd alone in the forest tree,
     Why, pretty thing! would you not live with me?
I kiss'd you oft, and gave you white peas;
Why not live sweetly, as in the green trees?

JOHN KEATS

30. SONG—THE OWL

When cats run home and light is come,
   And dew is cold upon the ground,
And the far-off stream is dumb,
    And the whirring sail goes round,
    And the whirring sail goes round;
      Alone and warming his five wits,
      The white owl in the belfry sits.

When merry milkmaids click the latch,
   And rarely smells the new-mown hay,
And the cock hath sung beneath the thatch
    Twice or thrice his roundelay,
    Twice or thrice his roundelay;
      Alone and warming his five wits,
      The white owl in the belfry sits.

ALFRED TENNYSON

31. DUCKS' DITTY

All along the backwater,
   Through the rushes tall,
Ducks are a-dabbling,
   Up tails all!

Ducks' tails, drakes' tails,
    Yellow feet a-quiver,
Yellow bills all out of sight
    Busy in the river!

Slushy green undergrowth
Where the roach swim—
Here we keep our larder
    Cool and full and dim!

Every one for what he likes!
We like to be
Heads down, tails up,
    Dabbling free!

High in the blue above
Swifts whirl and call—
We are down a-dabbling
    Up tails all!

KENNETH GRAHAME

32. THE CROW

Old crow, upon the tall tree-top
    I see you sitting at your ease,
You hang upon the highest bough,
    And balance in the breeze.

How many miles you've been to-day
    Upon your wing so strong and black,
And steered across the dark grey sky
    Without or guide or track;

Above the city wrapped in smoke,
    Green fields and rivers flowing clear;
Now tell me, as you passed them o'er
    What did you see and hear?

The old crow shakes his sooty wing,
    And answers, hoarsely, 'Caw, caw, caw,'
And that is all the crow can tell
    Of what he heard and saw.

MRS. ALEXANDER

33. OLD CROW

The bird in the corn
    Is a marvellous crow.
He was laid and was born
    In the season of snow;
And he chants his old catches
Like a ghost under hatches.

He comes from the shades
    Of his wood very early,
And works in the blades
    Of the wheat and the barley,
And he's happy, although
He's a grumbleton crow.

The larks have devices
    For sunny delight,
And the sheep in their fleeces
    Are woolly and white;
But these things are the scorn
Of the bird in the corn.

And morning goes by,
    And still he is there,
Till a rose in the sky
    Calls him back to his lair
In the boughs where the gloom
Is a part of his plume.

But the boy in the lane
    With his gun, by and by,
To the heart of the grain
    Will narrowly spy,
And the twilight will come,
And no crow will fly home.

JOHN DRINKWATER

34. NIGHT (EXTRACT)

The sun descending in the west,
The evening star does shine;
The birds are silent in their nest,
And I must seek for mine.
The moon, like a flower,
In heaven's high bower,
With silent delight
Sits and smiles on the night.

Farewell, green fields and happy groves,
Where flocks have took delight.
Where lambs have nibbled, silent moves
The feet of angels bright;
Unseen they pour blessing,
And joy without ceasing,
On each bud and blossom,
And each sleeping bosom.

36

They look in every thoughtless nest,
Where birds are cover'd warm;
They visit caves of every beast,
To keep them all from harm.
If they see any weeping
That should have been sleeping,
They pour sleep on their head,
And sit down by their bed.

WILLIAM BLAKE

35. TWILIGHT

The gentle Twilight Lady
   Is coming. Let her pass.
She scatters from her basket
   The dewdrops on the grass.
She closes up the lilies,
   She sends the bees to bed,
And throws a veil of silver
   Upon the rowans red.
And thro' the drowsy forest
   She bids the birds be still,
And listens, turns, and listens
   Unto the wakeful rill.
Then those who love the moortops,
   And to the hills belong,
May hear adown the valley
   The Twilight Lady's song,
Calling in lonely music,
   That breaks the heart o' the wild,
For Night, her star-eyed lover,
   To bring back Peace—their child.

DOROTHY UNA RATCLIFFE

36. TO THE LADY-BIRD

Lady-bird! Lady-bird! fly away home;
 The field-mouse is gone to her nest,
The daisies have shut up their sweet sleepy eyes,
 And the bees and the birds are at rest.

Lady-bird! Lady-bird! fly away home;
 The glow-worm is lighting her lamp,
The dew's falling fast, and your fine speckled wings
 Will be wet with the close-clinging damp.

Lady-bird! Lady-bird! fly away home;
 The fairy-bells tinkle afar;
Make haste, or they'll catch you, and harness you
  fast,
 With a cobweb, to Oberon's car.

37. OLD SHELLOVER

'Come!' said Old Shellover.
'What?' says Creep.
'The horny old Gardener's fast asleep;
The fat cock Thrush
To his nest has gone,
And the dew shines bright
In the rising Moon;
Old Sallie Worm from her hole doth peep;
Come!' said Old Shellover.
'Ay!' said Creep.

WALTER DE LA MARE

38. WYNKEN, BLYNKEN, AND NOD

Wynken, Blynken, and Nod one night
    Sailed off in a wooden shoe—
Sailed on a river of crystal light,
    Into a sea of dew.
'Where are you going, and what do you wish?'
    The old moon asked the three.
'We have come to fish for the herring fish
    That live in this beautiful sea;
    Nets of silver and gold have we!'
            Said Wynken,
            Blynken,
            And Nod.

The old moon laughed and sang a song,
    As they rocked in the wooden shoe,
And the wind that sped them all night long
    Ruffled the waves of dew.
The little stars were the herring fish
    That lived in that beautiful sea—
'Now cast your nets wherever you wish—
    Never afeared are we';
    So cried the stars to the fishermen three;
            Wynken,
            Blynken,
            And Nod.

All night long their nets they threw
    To the stars in the twinkling foam—
Then down from the skies came the wooden shoe,
    Bringing the fishermen home;
'Twas all so pretty a sail it seemed
    As if it could not be,

And some folks thought 'twas a dream they'd
    dreamed
  Of sailing that beautiful sea—
  But I shall name you the fishermen three:
     Wynken,
     Blynken,
     And Nod.

Wynken and Blynken are two little eyes,
  And Nod is a little head,
And the wooden shoe that sailed the skies
  Is a wee one's trundle-bed.
So shut your eyes while Mother sings
  Of wonderful sights that be,
And you shall see the beautiful things
  As you rock in the misty sea,
  Where the old shoe rocked the fishermen three:
     Wynken,
     Blynken,
     And Nod.

EUGENE FIELD

39. MINNIE AND WINNIE

Minnie and Winnie
  Slept in a shell.
Sleep, little ladies!
  And they slept well.

Pink was the shell within,
  Silver without,
Sounds of the great sea
  Wander'd about.

Sleep, little ladies!
  Wake not soon!
Echo on echo
  Dies to the moon.

Two bright stars
  Peep'd into the shell.
'What are they dreaming of?
  Who can tell?'

Started a green linnet
  Out of the croft;
Wake, little ladies,
  The sun is aloft!
                    ALFRED TENNYSON

40. THE MOON

Lady Moon, Lady Moon, where are you roving
        Over the sea.
Lady Moon, Lady Moon, whom are you loving?
        All that love me.

Are you not tired with rolling, and never
        Resting to sleep?
Why look so pale, and so sad, as for ever
        Wishing to weep?

Ask me not this, little child! if you love me;
        You are too bold;
I must obey my dear Father above me,
        And do as I'm told.

Lady Moon, Lady Moon, where are you roving?
  Over the sea.
Lady Moon, Lady Moon, whom are you loving?
  All that love me.

LORD HOUGHTON

4I. A RUNE OF RICHES

I have a golden ball,
A big, bright, shining one,
Pure gold; and it is all
Mine.—It is the sun.

I have a silver ball,
A white and glistering stone
That other people call
The moon;—my very own!

The jewel things that prick
My cushion's soft blue cover
Are mine,—my stars, thick, thick,
Scattered the sky all over.

And everything that's mine
Is yours, and yours, and yours,—
The shimmer and the shine!—
Let's lock our wealth out-doors!

FLORENCE CONVERSE

42. AT NIGHT

On moony nights the dogs bark shrill
Down the valley and up the hill.

There's one is angry to behold
The moon so unafraid and cold,
Who makes the earth as bright as day,
But yet unhappy, dead, and gray.

Another in his strawy lair
Says: 'Who's a-howling over there?
By heavens I will stop him soon
From interfering with the moon.'

So back he barks, with throat upthrown:
'You leave our moon, our moon alone.'
And other distant dogs respond
Beyond the fields, beyond, beyond.

FRANCES CORNFORD

43. THE HOUR OF NIGHT

Now came still Evening on, and Twilight grey
Had in her sober livery all things clad;
Silence accompanied, for beast and bird,
They to their grassy couch, these to their nests
Were slunk, all but the wakeful nightingale;
She all night long her amorous descant sung;
Silence was pleased: now glow'd the firmament
With living sapphires: Hesperus, that led
The starry host, rode brightest, till the Moon,
Rising in clouded majesty, at length
Apparent queen, unveil'd her peerless light,
And o'er the dark her silver mantle threw.

JOHN MILTON

44. THE NIGHTINGALE NEAR THE HOUSE

Here is the soundless cypress on the lawn:
It listens, listens. Taller trees beyond
Listen. The moon at the unruffled pond
    Stares. And you sing, you sing.

That star-enchanted song falls through the air
From lawn to lawn down terraces of sound,
Darts in white arrows on the shadowed ground;
    While all the night you sing.

My dreams are flowers to which you are a bee,
As all night long I listen, and my brain
Receives your song, then loses it again
    In moonlight on the lawn.

Now is your voice a marble high and white,
Then like a mist on fields of paradise;
Now is a raging fire, then is like ice,
    Then breaks, and it is dawn.

               HAROLD MONRO

45. HAPPY WIND

Oh, happy wind, how sweet
    Thy life must be!
The great, proud fields of gold
    Run after thee;
And here are flowers, with heads
    To nod and shake;
And dreaming butterflies
    To tease and wake.
Oh, happy wind, I say,
To be alive this day.

          WILLIAM H. DAVIES

46. THE RAIN

I hear leaves drinking rain;
 I hear rich leaves on top
Giving the poor beneath
 Drop after drop;
'Tis a sweet noise to hear
These green leaves drinking near.

And when the Sun comes out,
 After this rain shall stop,
A wondrous light will fill
 Each dark, round drop;
I hope the Sun shines bright;
'Twill be a lovely sight.

WILLIAM H. DAVIES

47. THE FOOLISH HAREBELL

A Harebell hung her wilful head:
'I am tired, so tired! I wish I was dead.'

She hung her head in the mossy dell:
'If all were over, then all were well!'

The Wind he heard, and was pitiful,
And waved her about to make her cool.

'Wind, you are rough!' said the dainty Bell;
'Leave me alone—I am not well.'

The Wind, at the word of the drooping dame,
Sighed to himself and ceased in shame.

'I am hot, so hot!' she moaned and said;
'I am withering up; I wish I was dead!'

Then the Sun he pitied her woeful case,
And drew a thick veil over his face.

'Cloud go away, and don't be rude,'
She said; 'I do not see why you should!'

The Cloud withdrew. Then the Harebell cried,
'I am faint, so faint!—and no water beside!'

The Dew came down its millionfold path:
She murmured, 'I did not want a bath!'

The Dew went up; the Wind softly crept;
The Night came down, and the Harebell slept.

A boy ran past in the morning gray,
Plucked the Harebell, and threw her away.

The Harebell shivered, and sighed, 'Oh! oh!
I am faint indeed! Come, dear Wind, blow.'

The Wind blew gently, and did not speak.
She thanked him kindly, but grew more weak.

'Sun, dear Sun, I am cold!' she said.
He shone; but lower she drooped her head.

'Oh Rain, I am withering! all the blue
Is fading out of me!—come, please do!'

The Rain came down as fast as he could,
But for all his good will he could do her no good.

She shuddered and shrivelled, and moaning said,
'Thank you all kindly!' and then she was dead.

Let us hope, let us hope when she comes next year
She'll be simple and sweet! But I fear, I fear!

GEORGE MACDONALD

48. FOUR AND EIGHT

The Foxglove by the cottage door
Looks down on Joe, and Joe is Four.

The Foxglove by the garden gate
Looks down on Joan, and Joan is Eight.

'I'm glad we're small,' said Joan, 'I love
To see inside the fox's glove,
Where taller people cannot see,
And all is ready for the bee;
The door is wide, the feast is spread,
The walls are dotted rosy red;'
'And only little people know
How nice it looks in there,' said Joe.
Said Joan, 'The upper rooms are locked;
A bee went buzzing up—he knocked,
But no one let him in, so then
He bumbled gaily down again.'
'Oh, dear!' sighed Joe, 'if only we
Could grow as little as that bee,
We too might room by room explore
The Foxglove by the cottage door.'

The Foxglove by the garden gate
Looked down and smiled on Four and Eight.

FFRIDA WOLFE

49. POPPIES

The poppies in the garden, they all wear frocks of
    silk,
Some are purple, some are pink, and others white
    as milk,
Light, light for dancing in—for dancing when the
    breeze
Plays a little two-step for the blossoms and the bees:
Fine, fine for dancing—all frilly at the hem,
Oh! when I watch the poppies dance I long to dance
    like them.

The poppies in the garden have let their silk frocks
    fall
All about the border paths; but where are they at
    all?
Here a frill, and there a flounce—a rag of silky red,
But not a poppy-girl is left; I think they've gone to
    bed;
Gone to bed and gone to sleep and weary they must
    be,
For each has left her box of dreams up on the stem
    for me.

FFRIDA WOLFE

50. THISTLEDOWN

They grip their withered edge of stalk
In brief excitement for the wind;
They hold a breathless final talk,
And when their filmy cables part
One almost hears a little cry.

Some cling together while they wait
And droop and gaze and hesitate,
But others leap along the sky,
Or circle round and calmly choose
The gust they know they ought to use.

While some in loving pairs will glide,
Or watch the others as they pass,
Or rest on flowers in the grass,
Or circle through the shining day
Like silver butterflies at play.

Some catch themselves to every mound,
Then lingeringly and slowly move
As if they knew the precious ground
Were opening for their fertile love:
They almost try to dig, they need
So much to plant their thistle-seed.

HAROLD MONRO

5I. THE CATERPILLAR

Brown and furry
Caterpillar, in a hurry
Take your walk
To the shady leaf or stalk
Or what not,
Which may be the chosen spot.
No toad spy you,
Hovering bird of prey pass by you;
Spin and die,
To live again a butterfly.

CHRISTINA ROSSETTI

52. THE WASP

Where the ripe pears droop heavily
    The yellow wasp hums loud and long
    His hot and drowsy autumn song:
A yellow flame he seems to be,
    When darting suddenly from high
    He lights where fallen peaches lie:

    Yellow and black, this tiny thing's
    A tiger soul on elfin wings.

WILLIAM SHARP

53. ALMS IN AUTUMN

Spindle-wood, spindle-wood, will you lend me,
    pray,
A little flaming lantern to light me on my way?
The fairy folk have vanished from the meadow and
    the glen,
And I would fain go seeking till I find them once
    again;
Lend me now a lantern that I may bear a light
To show the hidden pathway in the darkness of the
    night.

Ash tree, ash tree, throw me, if you please,
Throw me down a slender bunch of russet-gold
    keys;
I fear the gates of fairyland may all be shut fast;
Give me of your magic keys that I may get past;
I'll tie them to my girdle, that as I go along
My heart may find a comfort in their tiny tinkling
    song.

50

Holly bush, holly bush, help me in my task,
A pocketful of berries is all the alms I ask;
A pocketful of berries to thread in glowing strands
(I would not go a-visiting with nothing in my
    hands);
So fine will be the rosy chains, so gay, so glossy
    bright,
They'll set the realms of fairyland a-dancing with
    delight.

ROSE FYLEMAN

54. SCARLETT'S SONG

'Sing a song of scarlet poppies in the corn,
Sing a song of rosy blossoms on the thorn;
Sing a song of robins chirping all the day
When nests are empty and the skies are gray.

Sing a song of scarlet hips upon the brier,
Sing a song of dead boughs reddening in the fire;
Sing a song of red suns, frost and tingling blood,
Sing a song of autumn flushing all the wood.

Sing a song of Scarlett when the frosts begin,
Heaping on the camp-fire store of prickly whin;
Sing a song of Marian laughing through the wood,
Sing a song of roses grown for Robin Hood.'

NORA CHESSON

55. OCTOBER

(From 'The Months: a Pageant')

I've brought you nuts and hops;
And when the leaf drops, why, the walnut drops.
Crack your first nut and light your first fire,
    Roast your first chestnut crisp on the bar;
Make the logs sparkle, stir the blaze higher,
      Logs are as cheery as sun or as star,
      Logs we can find wherever we are.
Spring one soft day will open the leaves,
    Spring one bright day will lure back the flowers;
Never fancy my whistling wind grieves,
    Never fancy I've tears in my showers:
    Dance, nights and days! and dance on, my hours!

CHRISTINA ROSSETTI

56. WINTER

Sweet blackbird is silenced with chaffinch and
    thrush,
Only waistcoated robin still chirps in the bush:
Soft sun-loving swallows have mustered in force,
And winged to the spice-teeming southlands their
    course.

Plump housekeeper dormouse has tucked himself
    neat,
Just a brown ball in moss with a morsel to eat:
Armed hedgehog has huddled him into the hedge,
While frogs scarce miss freezing deep down in the
    sedge.

Soft swallows have left us alone in the lurch,
But robin sits whistling to us from his perch:
If I were red robin, I'd pipe you a tune,
Would make you despise all the beauties of June.

But, since that cannot be, let us draw round the fire,
Munch chestnuts, tell stories, and stir the blaze
    higher:
We'll comfort pinched robin with crumbs, little
    man,
Till he'll sing us the very best song that he can.

CHRISTINA ROSSETTI

57. THE BABES IN THE WOOD

My dear, do you know
How a long time ago,
Two poor little children
Whose names I don't know,
Were stolen away
On a fine summer's day,
And left in a wood,
As I've heard people say;

And when it was night,
So sad was their plight,
The sun it went down
And the moon gave no light!
They sobbed and they sighed
And they bitterly cried,
And the poor little things,
They lay down and died.

And when they were dead,
The robins so red
Brought strawberry leaves,
And over them spread;
And all the day long
They sang them this song—
'Poor babes in the wood!
Poor babes in the wood!
And don't you remember
The babes in the wood?'

58. ROBIN REDBREAST

Good-bye, good-bye to Summer!
   For Summer's nearly done;
The garden smiling faintly,
   Cool breezes in the sun;
Our thrushes now are silent,
   Our swallows flown away,—
But Robin's here in coat of brown,
   With ruddy breast-knot gay.
     Robin, Robin Redbreast,
     O Robin dear!
     Robin singing sweetly
     In the falling year.

Bright yellow, red, and orange,
   The leaves come down in hosts;
The trees are Indian Princes,
   But soon they'll turn to Ghosts;
The scanty pears and apples
   Hang russet on the bough;
It's Autumn, Autumn, Autumn late
   'Twill soon be Winter now.

Robin, Robin Redbreast,
O Robin dear!
And welladay! my Robin,
For pinching times are near.

The fireside for the Cricket,
The wheatstack for the Mouse,
When trembling night-winds whistle
And moan all round the house;
The frosty ways like iron,
The branches plumed with snow,—
Alas! in Winter, dead and dark,
Where can poor Robin go?
Robin, Robin Redbreast,
O Robin, dear!
And a crumb of bread for Robin,
His little heart to cheer.

WILLIAM ALLINGHAM

59. ROBIN REDBREAST

Robin on a leafless bough,
Lord in Heaven, how he sings!
Now cold Winter's cruel Wind
Makes playmates of withered things.

How he sings for joy this morn!
How his breast doth pant and glow!
Look you how he stands and sings,
Half-way up his legs in snow!

If these crumbs of bread were pearls,
And I had no bread at home,

55

He should have them for that song;
Pretty Robin Redbreast, come.

WILLIAM H. DAVIES

60. THE NORTH WIND

The North wind doth blow,
And we shall have snow,
And what will the robin do then, poor thing?
O, he'll go to the barn,
And to keep himself warm
He'll hide his head under his wing, poor thing.

The North wind doth blow,
And we shall have snow,
And what will the swallow do then, poor thing?
O, do you not know
He's gone long ago
To a country much warmer than ours, poor thing?

The North wind doth blow,
And we shall have snow,
And what will the dormouse do then, poor thing?
Rolled up in a ball,
In his nest snug and small,
He'll sleep till the winter is past, poor thing.

The North wind doth blow,
And we shall have snow,
And what will the children do then, poor things?
O! when lessons are done,
They'll jump, skip and run,
And play till they make themselves warm, poor
things.

OLD RHYME

6I. WINTER

When icicles hang by the wall,
    And Dick the shepherd blows his nail,
And Tom bears logs into the hall,
    And milk comes frozen home in pail,
When blood is nipt, and ways be foul,
    Then nightly sings the staring owl,
              Tu-who;
Tu-whit, Tu-who—a merry note,
While greasy Joan doth keel the pot.

When all around the wind doth blow,
    And coughing drowns the parson's saw,
And birds sit brooding in the snow,
    And Marian's nose looks red and raw,
When roasted crabs hiss in the bowl,
    Then nightly sings the staring owl,
              Tu-who;
Tu-whit, Tu-who—a merry note,
While greasy Joan doth keel the pot.

WILLIAM SHAKESPEARE

62. WINTER

(From 'The Window; or, The Song of the Wrens')

The frost is here,
The fuel is dear,
And woods are sear,
And fires burn clear,
And frost is here
And has bitten the heel of the going year.

Bite, frost, bite!
You roll up away from the light,
The blue wood-louse and the plump dormouse,
And the bees are still'd and the flies are kill'd,
And you bite far into the heart of the house,
But not into mine.

Bite, frost, bite!
The woods are all the searer,
The fuel is all the dearer,
The fires are all the clearer,
My spring is all the nearer,
You have bitten into the heart of the earth,
But not into mine.

ALFRED TENNYSON

63. CAROL

When the herds were watching
In the midnight chill,
Came a spotless lambkin
From the heavenly hill.

Snow was on the mountains,
And the wind was cold,
When from God's own garden
Dropped a rose of gold.

When 'twas bitter winter,
Houseless and forlorn,
In a star-lit stable
Christ the Babe was born.

58

Welcome, heavenly lambkin;
Welcome golden rose;
Alleluia, Baby
In the swaddling clothes.

WILLIAM CANTON

64. CAROL

In the bleak mid-winter
    Frosty wind made moan,
Earth stood hard as iron,
    Water like a stone:
Snow had fallen, snow on snow,
    Snow on snow,
In the bleak mid-winter,
    Long ago.

Our God, heaven cannot hold Him
    Nor earth sustain;
Heaven and earth shall flee away
    When He comes to reign:
In the bleak mid-winter
    A stable place sufficed
The Lord God Almighty,
    Jesus Christ.

Enough for Him, whom Cherubim
    Worship night and day,
A breastful of milk
    And a mangerful of hay;
Enough for Him, whom angels
    Fall down before,
The ox and ass and camel
    Which adore.

59

Angels and Archangels
   May have gathered there,
Cherubim and Seraphim
   Thronged the air—
But only His mother
   In her maiden bliss
Worshipped the Belovèd
   With a kiss.

What can I give Him
   Poor as I am?
If I were a shepherd
   I would bring a lamb:
If I were a wise man
   I would do my part:
Yet what I can I give Him—
   Give my heart.

CHRISTINA ROSSETTI

65. THE STAR SONG: A CAROL TO THE KING

Tell us, thou clear and heavenly tongue,
Where is the Babe but lately sprung?
Lies He the lily-banks among?

Or say; if this new Birth of ours
Sleeps, laid within some ark of flowers,
Spangled with dew-light; thou canst clear
All doubts, and manifest the where.

Declare to us, bright star, if we shall seek
Him in the morning's blushing cheek,
Or search the bed of spices through
To find Him out?

60

Star: No, this you need not do;
But only come and see Him rest;
A princely Babe, in's mother's breast.

CHORUS: *He's seen! He's seen! Why then around*
Let's kiss the sweet and holy ground;
And all rejoice that we have found
A King before conception crown'd.

Come then, come then, and let us bring
Unto our pretty Twelfth-Tide King
Each one his several offering;

CHORUS: *And when night comes we'll give him*
wassailing:
And that His treble honours may be seen,
We'll choose Him King, and make His mother
Queen.

ROBERT HERRICK

66. THE BIRDS

When Jesus Christ was four years old,
The angels brought Him toys of gold,
Which no man ever had bought or sold.

And yet with these He would not play.
He made Him small fowl out of clay,
And blessed them till they flew away:
Tu creasti Domine.

Jesus Christ, Thou child so wise,
Bless mine hands and fill mine eyes,
And bring my soul to Paradise.

HILAIRE BELLOC

67. A CHILD'S DREAM

I had a little dog, and my dog was very small;
He licked me in the face, and he answered to my
    call;
Of all the treasures that were mine, I loved him
    most of all.

His nose was fresh as morning dew and blacker
    than the night;
I thought that it could even snuff the shadows and
    the light;
And his tail he held bravely, like a banner in a fight.

His body covered thick with hair was very good to
    smell;
His little stomach underneath was pink as any shell;
And I loved him and honoured him, more than
    words can tell.

We ran out in the morning, both of us, to play,
Up and down across the fields for all the sunny day;
But he ran so swiftly—he ran right away.

I looked for him, I called him, entreatingly. Alas,
The dandelions could not speak, though they had
    seen him pass,
And nowhere was his waving tail among the waving
    grass.

I called him in a thousand ways and yet he did not
    come;
The pathways and the hedges were horrible and
    dumb.
I prayed to God who never heard. My desperate
    soul grew numb.

The sun sank low. I ran; I prayed: 'If God has not
    the power
To find him, let me die. I cannot bear another
    hour.'
When suddenly I came upon a great yellow flower.

And all among its petals, such was Heaven's grace,
In that golden hour, in that golden place,
All among its petals, was his hairy face.
FRANCES CORNFORD

68. THE LAMPLIGHTER

My tea is nearly ready and the sun has left the sky;
It's time to take the window to see Leerie going by;
For every night at tea-time and before you take
    your seat,
With lantern and with ladder he comes posting up
    the street.

Now Tom would be a driver and Maria go to sea,
And my papa's a banker and as rich as he can be;
But I, when I am stronger and can choose what I'm
    to do,
Oh, Leerie, I'll go round at night and light the
    lamps with you!

For we are very lucky, with a lamp before the door;
And Leerie stops to light it as he lights so many
    more,
And O! before you hurry by with ladder and with
    light,
O Leerie, see a little child and nod to him to-night!
ROBERT LOUIS STEVENSON

69. THE PEDLAR'S CARAVAN

I wish I lived in a caravan,
With a horse to drive, like a pedlar man!
Where he comes from nobody knows,
Nor where he goes to, but on he goes.

His caravan has windows two,
With a chimney of tin that the smoke comes
    through.
He has a wife and a baby brown,
And they go riding from town to town.

Chairs to mend and delf to sell—
He clashes the basins like a bell.
Tea-trays, baskets, ranged in order,
Plates, with the alphabet round the border.

The roads are brown, and the sea is green,
But his house is just like a bathing machine.
The world is round, but he can ride
Rumble, and splash to the other side.

With the pedlar-man I should like to roam,
And write a book when I come home.
All the people would read my book,
Just like the Travels of Captain Cook.

W. B. RANDS

70. MY SHADOW

I have a little shadow that goes in and out with me,
And what can be the use of him is more than I can
    see.

He is very, very like me from the heels up to the
    head;
And I see him jump before me, when I jump into
    my bed.

The funniest thing about him is the way he likes to
    grow—
Not at all like proper children, which is always very
    slow;
For he sometimes shoots up taller like an india-
    rubber ball,
And he sometimes gets so little that there's none of
    him at all.

He hasn't got a notion of how children ought to play,
And can only make a fool of me in every sort of way.
He stays so close beside me, he's a coward you can
    see;
I'd think it shame to stick to nursie as that shadow
    sticks to me!

One morning, very early, before the sun was up,
I rose and found the shining dew on every buttercup;
But my lazy little shadow, like an arrant sleepy-
    head
Had stayed at home behind me and was fast asleep
    in bed.

ROBERT LOUIS STEVENSON

71. THE SWING

How do you like to go up in a swing,
Up in the air so blue?
Oh, I do think it the pleasantest thing
Ever a child can do!

65

Up in the air and over the wall,
Till I can see so wide,
Rivers and trees and cattle and all
Over the countryside—

Till I look down on the garden green,
Down on the roof so brown—
Up in the air I go flying again,
Up in the air and down!

ROBERT LOUIS STEVENSON

72. THE NIGHT WIND

Have you ever heard the wind go 'Yooooo'?
'Tis a pitiful sound to hear!
It seems to chill you through and through
With a strange and speechless fear.
'Tis the voice of the night that broods outside
When folk should be asleep,
And many and many's the time I've cried
To the darkness brooding far and wide
Over the land and the deep:
'Whom do you want, O lonely night,
That you wail the long hours through?'
And the night would say in its ghostly way:
      'Yoooooooo!
      Yoooooooo!
      Yoooooooo!'

My mother told me long ago
(When I was a little lad)
That when the night went wailing so,
Somebody had been bad;

66

And then, when I was snug in bed,
Whither I had been sent,
With the blankets pulled up round my head,
I'd think of what my mother'd said,
And wonder what boy she meant!
And 'Who's been bad to-day?' I'd ask
Of the wind that hoarsely blew,
And the voice would say in its meaningful way:
   'Yoooooooo!
   Yoooooooo!
   Yoooooooo!'

That this was true I must allow—
You'll not believe it, though!
Yes, though I'm quite a model now,
I was not always so.
And if you doubt the things I say
Suppose you make the test;
Suppose, when you've been bad some day
And up to bed are sent away
From mother and the rest—
Suppose you ask, 'Who has been bad?'
And then you'll hear what's true;
For the wind will moan in its ruefullest tone:
   'Yoooooooo!
   Yoooooooo!
   Yoooooooo!'

EUGENE FIELD

73. TIRED TIM

Poor tired Tim! It's sad for him.
He lags the long bright morning through,
Ever so tired of nothing to do;

He moons and mopes the livelong day,
Nothing to think about, nothing to say;
Up to bed with his candle to creep,
Too tired to yawn, too tired to sleep:
Poor tired Tim! It's sad for him.

WALTER DE LA MARE

74. STORY OF JOHNNY HEAD-IN-AIR

As he trudged along to school,
It was always Johnny's rule
To be looking at the sky
And the clouds that floated by;
But what just before him lay,
In his way,
Johnny never thought about;
So that everyone cried out:
'Look at little Johnny there,
Little Johnny Head-in-Air!'

Running just in Johnny's way,
Came a little dog one day;
Johnny's eyes were still astray
Up on high,
In the sky;
And he never heard them cry:
'Johnny, mind, the dog is nigh!'
Bump!
Dump!
Down they fell with such a thump
Dog and Johnny in a lump!

68

Once, with head as high as ever,
Johnny walked beside the river.
Johnny watched the swallows trying
Which was cleverest at flying.
Oh! what fun!
Johnny watched the bright round sun
Going in and coming out;
This was all he thought about.
So he strode on, only think!
To the river's very brink,
Where the bank was high and steep,
And the water very deep;
And the fishes, in a row,
Stared to see him coming so.

One step more! Oh! sad to tell!
Headlong in poor Johnny fell.
And the fishes, in dismay,
Wagged their tails and swam away.
There lay Johnny on his face,
With his nice red writing-case;
But, as they were passing by,
Two strong men had heard him cry;
And, with sticks, these two strong men
Hooked poor Johnny out again.

Oh! you should have seen him shiver
When they pulled him from the river.
He was in a sorry plight!
Dripping wet, and such a fright!
Wet all over, everywhere,
Clothes, and arms, and face, and hair:
Johnny never will forget
What it is to be so wet.

And the fishes, one, two, three
Are come back again, you see;
Up they came the moment after,
To enjoy the fun and laughter.
Each popped out his little head,
And to tease poor Johnny, said:
'Silly little Johnny, look,
You have lost your writing-book!'

HEINRICH HOFFMANN

75. STORY OF AUGUSTUS WHO WOULD NOT HAVE ANY SOUP

Augustus was a chubby lad!
Fat, ruddy cheeks Augustus had;
And everybody saw with joy
The plump and hearty, healthy boy.
He ate and drank as he was told,
And never let his soup get cold.
But one day, one cold winter's day,
He screamed out: 'Take the soup away!
O take the nasty soup away!
I won't have any soup to-day.'

Next day, now look, the picture shows
How lank and lean Augustus grows!
Yet though he feels so weak and ill,
The naughty fellow cries out still:
'Not any soup for me, I say:
O take the nasty soup away!
I won't have any soup to-day.'

The third day comes; O what a sin!
To make himself so pale and thin.
Yet, when the soup is put on table,
He screams, as loud as he is able:
'Not any soup for me, I say:
O take the nasty soup away!
I won't have any soup to-day.'

Look at him now the fourth day's come!
He scarcely weighs a sugar-plum;
He's like a little bit of thread,
And on the fifth day, he was—dead!

HEINRICH HOFFMANN

76. POOR HENRY

Thick in its glass
    The physic stands,
Poor Henry lifts
    Distracted hands;
His round cheek wans
    In the candlelight,
To smell that smell!
    To see that sight!

Finger and thumb
    Clinch his small nose,
A gurgle, a gasp,
    And down it goes;
Scowls Henry now;
    But mark that cheek,
Sleek with the bloom
    Of health next week!

WALTER DE LA MARE

71

77. DAME WIGGINS OF LEE

PART I

Dame Wiggins of Lee
Was a worthy old soul,
As e'er threaded a nee-
dle, or wash'd in a bowl;
She held mice and rats
In such antipa-thy,
That seven fine cats
Kept Dame Wiggins of Lee.

The rats and mice scared
By this fierce whisker'd crew,
The poor seven cats
Soon had nothing to do;
So, as anyone idle
She ne'er loved to see,
She sent them to school,
Did Dame Wiggins of Lee.

But soon she grew tired
Of living alone;
So she sent for her cats
From school to come home.
Each rowing a wherry,
Returning you see:
The frolic made merry
Dame Wiggins of Lee.

The Dame was quite pleas'd
And ran out to Market;
When she came back
They were mending the carpet.

The needle each handled
As brisk as a bee;
'Well done, my good cats,'
Said Dame Wiggins of Lee.

To give them a treat,
She ran out for some rice;
When she came back,
They were skating on ice.
'I shall soon see one down,
Aye, perhaps, two or three,
I'll bet half a crown,'
Said Dame Wiggins of Lee.

They called the next day
On the tomtit and sparrow,
And wheeled a poor sick lamb
Home in a barrow.
'You shall all have some sprats
For your humani-ty,
My seven good cats,'
Said Dame Wiggins of Lee.

While she ran to the field,
To look for its dam,
They were warming the bed
For the poor sick lamb:
They turn'd up the clothes
All as neat as could be;
'I shall ne'er want a nurse,'
Said Dame Wiggins of Lee.

She wished them good night,
And went up to bed:
When, lo! in the morning,
The cats were all fled.

But soon—what a fuss:
'Where can they all be?
Here, pussy, puss, puss!'
Cried Dame Wiggins of Lee.

The Dame's heart was nigh broke
So she sat down to weep,
When she saw them come back
Each riding a sheep:
She fondled and patted
Each purring tom-my:
'Ah! welcome, my dears,'
Said Dame Wiggins of Lee

The Dame was unable
Her pleasure to smother,
To see the sick lamb
Jump up to its mother.
In spite of the gout,
And a pain in her knee,
She went dancing about:
Did Dame Wiggins of Lee.

The Farmer soon heard
Where his sheep went astray,
And arrived at Dame's door
With his faithful dog Tray.
He knocked with his crook,
And the stranger to see,
Out the window did look
Dame Wiggins of Lee.

74

For their kindness he had them
All drawn by his team;
And gave them some field-mice
And raspberry-cream.
Said he, 'All my stock
You shall presently see;
For I honour the cats
Of Dame Wiggins of Lee.'

He sent his maid out
For some muffins and crumpets;
And when he turn'd round
They were blowing of trumpets.
Said he, 'I suppose
She's as deaf as can be,
Or this ne'er could be borne
By Dame Wiggins of Lee.'

To show them his poultry,
He turn'd them all loose,
When each nimbly leap'd
On the back of a goose,
Which frightened them so
That they ran to the sea,
And half-drown'd the poor cats
Of Dame Wiggins of Lee.

For the care of his lamb,
And their comical pranks,
He gave them a ham
And abundance of thanks.
'I wish you good-day,
My fine fellows,' said he;
'My compliments, pray,
To Dame Wiggins of Lee.'

You see them arrived
At their Dame's welcome door;
They show her their presents
And all their good store.
'Now come in to supper,
And sit down with me;
All welcome once more,'
Cried Dame Wiggins of Lee.

78. MILK FOR THE CAT

When the tea is brought at five o'clock,
And all the neat curtains are drawn with care,
The little black cat with bright green eyes
Is suddenly purring there.

At first she pretends, having nothing to do,
She has come in merely to blink by the grate,
Yet, though tea may be late or the milk may be sour,
She is never late.

And presently her agate eyes
Take a soft large milky haze,
And her independent casual glance
Becomes a stiff hard gaze.

Then she stamps her claws or lifts her ears,
Or twists her tail and begins to stir,
Till suddenly all her lithe body becomes
One breathing trembling purr.

The children eat and wriggle and laugh;
The two old ladies stroke their silk;
But the cat is grown small and thin with desire,
Transformed to a creeping lust for milk.

The white saucer like some full moon descends
At last from the clouds of the table above;
She sighs and dreams and thrills and glows,
Transfigured with love.

She nestles over the shining rim,
Buries her chin in the creamy sea;
Her tail hangs loose; each drowsy paw
Is doubled under each bending knee.

A long dim ecstasy holds her life:
Her world is an infinite shapeless white,
Till her tongue has curled the last half drop,
Then she sinks back into the night,

Draws and dips her body to heap
Her sleepy nerves in the great arm-chair,
Lies defeated and buried deep
Three or four hours unconscious there.

HAROLD MONRO

79. THE DUEL

The gingham dog and the calico cat
Side by side on the table sat;
'Twas half-past twelve and (what do you think?)
Nor one nor t'other had slept a wink!
The old Dutch clock and the Chinese plate
Appeared to know as sure as fate
There was going to be a terrible spat.
(I wasn't there; I simply state
What was told to me by the Chinese plate!)

The gingham dog went 'bow-wow-wow!'
And the calico cat replied 'Mee-ow!'
The air was littered, an hour or so,
With bits of gingham and calico,
While the old Dutch clock in the chimney-place
Up with its hands before its face
For it always dreaded a family row!
(Now mind: I'm only telling you
What the old Dutch clock declares is true!)

The Chinese plate looked very blue
And wailed 'Oh, dear! What shall we do?'
But the gingham dog and the calico cat
Wallowed this way and tumbled that,
Employing every tooth and claw
In the awfullest way you ever saw—
And oh! how the gingham and calico flew
(Don't fancy I exaggerate!
I got my news from the Chinese plate!)

Next morning where the two had sat,
They found no trace of dog or cat;
And some folks think unto this day
That burglars stole the pair away!
But the truth about the cat and pup
Is this: they ate each other up!
Now what do you really think of that?
(The old Dutch clock it told me so
And that is how I came to know.)

                                    EUGENE FIELD

80. THE MOUNTAIN AND THE SQUIRREL

The mountain and the squirrel
Had a quarrel;
And the former called the latter, 'Little prig.'
Bun replied,
'You are doubtless very big;
But all sorts of things and weather
Must be taken in together,
To make up a year
And a sphere.
And I think it no disgrace
To occupy my place.
If I'm not so large as you,
You are not so small as I,
And not half so spry.
I'll not deny you make
A very pretty squirrel track;
Talents differ; all is well and wisely put;
If I cannot carry forests on my back,
Neither can you crack a nut.'

RALPH WALDO EMERSON

81. THE WIND IN A FROLIC

The wind one morning sprang up from sleep,
Saying, 'Now for a frolic! now for a leap!
Now for a mad-cap galloping chase!
I'll make a commotion in every place!'
So it swept with a bustle right through the town,
Cracking the signs and scattering down
Shutters; and whisking, with merciless squalls,
Old women's bonnets and gingerbread stalls.

There never was heard a much lustier shout,
As the apples and oranges trundled about;
And the urchins that stand with their thievish eyes
For ever on watch, ran off each with a prize.

Then away to the fields it went, blustering and
        humming,
And the cattle all wondered whatever was coming;
It plucked by the tails the grave matronly cows,
And tossed the colts' manes all over their brows;
Till offended at such an unusual salute,
They all turned their backs, and stood sulky and
        mute.

Then it rushed like a monster on cottage and farm,
Striking their dwellers with sudden alarm;
And they ran out like bees in a midsummer
        swarm;—
There were dames with their kerchiefs tied over
        their caps,
To see if their poultry were free from mishaps;
The turkeys they gobbled, the geese screamed
        aloud;
The hens crept to roost in a terrified crowd;
There was rearing of ladders, and logs laying on,
Where the thatch from the roof threatened soon to
        be gone.

But the wind had swept on, and had met in a lane
With a schoolboy, who panted and struggled in
        vain;
For it tossed him and twirled him, then passed and
        he stood
With his hat in a pool and his shoes in the mud.

Then away went the wind in its holiday glee,
And now it was far on the billowy sea,
And the lordly ships felt its staggering blow,
And the little boats darted to and fro.
But lo! it was night, and it sank to rest
On the sea-bird's rock in the gleaming west,
Laughing to think, in its fearful fun,
How little of mischief it really had done.

WILLIAM HOWITT

82. WISHING

Ring-ting! I wish I were a Primrose,
A bright yellow Primrose, blowing in the Spring!
    The stooping boughs above me,
    The wandering bee to love me,
  The fern and moss to creep across,
    And the Elm-tree for our King!

Nay—stay! I wish I were an Elm-tree,
A great lofty Elm-tree, with green leaves gay!
    The winds would set them dancing,
    The sun and moonshine glancing,
  The Birds would house among the boughs,
    And sweetly sing!

O—no! I wish I were a Robin,
A Robin or a little Wren, everywhere to go;
    Through forest, field, or garden,
    And ask no leave or pardon,
  Till Winter comes with icy thumbs
    To ruffle up our wing!

F

Well—tell! Where should I fly to?
Where go to sleep in the dark wood or dell?
　　Before a day was over,
　　Home comes the rover,
　For Mother's kiss,—sweeter this
　　Than any other thing!

WILLIAM ALLINGHAM

83. THE ALL ALONE TREE

There's a tree that is growing alone on the hill,
By the path that winds up at the back of the mill,
And we're awfully fond of it, Maudie and me,
And we call it the All Alone, All Alone Tree.

It is old, and it's wrinkled and twisted and dry
And it grows by itself with no other tree nigh,
And we always sit under it, Maudie and me,
Because it's the All Alone, All Alone Tree.

In the bright summer-time when they're cutting
　　the hay,
Then the birds come and sing in its branches all
　　day,
And we're awfully glad of this, Maudie and me,
Because it's the All Alone, All Alone Tree.

But in the dark winter the birds have all flown,
And we know that it's standing there, quite, quite
　　alone,
So we creep out and kiss it then, Maudie and me,
Because it's the All Alone, All Alone Tree.

F. O'NEILL GALLAGHER

82

84. THE APPOINTMENT

Tree! you are years standing there,
   Gripping tight to the side of the hill,
And your branches are spread on the air,
   While you stand so sad and so still,
     And you do not complain
     When you're wet with the rain,
   Though I think you have often been ill.

I would like (but it could not be done,
   So you must not keep me to my word)
To take you away when the sun
   Goes down, and the breezes are stirred,
     And hug you in bed
     With myself, till you said
   That to sleep on a hill was absurd.

O beautiful tree! when the night
   Is dark, and the winds come and scold,
I would love then to cuddle you tight,
   For I fear you will die of the cold;
     But you are so tall,
     And my bed is so small,
   That it could not be done, I am told.

My mother is calling for me,
   And the baby is wanting to play,
I shall have to go home now, you see,
   But I'll give you a kiss if I may:
     I would stay if I could,
     But a child must be good,
   So I must, darling tree, go away.

I will leave you my pencil and slate,
   And this little pin from my frock;
But now I must go, for it's late,
   And my mother is rattling the lock:
     So good-bye, darling dear,
     I'll come back, never fear,
In the morning at seven o'clock.

JAMES STEPHENS

85. BABY

Where did you come from, baby dear?
Out of everywhere into here.

Where did you get those eyes so blue?
Out of the sky as I came through.

What makes the light in them sparkle and spin?
Some of the starry twinkles left in.

Where did you get that little tear?
I found it waiting when I got here.

What makes your forehead so smooth and high?
A soft hand stroked it as I went by.

What makes your cheek like a warm white rose?
I saw something better than anyone knows.

Whence that three-cornered smile of bliss?
Three angels gave me at once a kiss.

Where did you get this pearly ear?
God spoke, and it came out to hear.

84

Where did you get those arms and hands?
Love made itself into bonds and bands.

Feet, whence did you come, you darling things?
From the same box as the cherubs' wings.

How did they all just come to be you?
God thought about me, and so I grew.

But how did you come to us, you dear?
God thought about you, and so I am here.

GEORGE MACDONALD

86. A LITTLE MISTAKE

I studied my tables over and over, and backward
    and forward, too;
But I couldn't remember six times nine, and I
    didn't know what to do,
Till sister told me to play with my doll, and not to
    bother my head.
'If you call her "Fifty-four" for a while, you'll learn
    it by heart,' she said.

So I took my favourite Mary Ann (though I thought
    'twas a dreadful shame
To give such a perfectly lovely child such a perfectly
    horrid name),
And I called her my dear little 'Fifty-four' a hun-
    dred times, till I knew
The answer of six times nine as well as the answer
    of two times two.

Next day, Elizabeth Wigglesworth, who always
    seems so proud,
Said, 'Six times nine is fifty-two,' and I nearly
    laughed aloud!
But I wished I hadn't when teacher said, 'Now,
    Dorothy, tell if you can,'
For I thought of my doll, and——oh dear me!——
    I answered 'Mary Ann!'

ANNA M. PRATT

87. THE LOST DOLL

I once had a sweet little doll, dears,
    The prettiest doll in the world;
Her cheeks were so red and so white, dears,
    And her hair was so charmingly curled.
But I lost my poor little doll, dears,
    As I played in the heath one day;
And I cried for more than a week, dears,
    But I never could find where she lay.

I found my poor little doll, dears,
    As I played in the heath one day;
Folks say she is terribly changed, dears,
    For her paint is all washed away,
And her arm trodden off by the cows, dears,
    And her hair not the least bit curled:
Yet for old sakes' sake she is still, dears,
    The prettiest doll in the world.

CHARLES KINGSLEY

88. THE VULGAR LITTLE LADY

Mamma now, said Charlotte, Pray, don't you believe
    That I'm better than Jenny, my nurse?
Only see my red shoes, and the lace on my sleeve;
    Her clothes are a thousand times worse.

I ride in my coach, and have nothing to do,
    And the country folk stare at me so,
And nobody dares to control me but you,
    Because I'm a lady, you know.

Then, servants are vulgar, and I am genteel;
    So really, 'tis out of the way,
To think that I should not be better a deal
    Than maids, and such people as they.

Gentility, Charlotte, her mother replied,
    Belongs to no station or place;
And nothing's so vulgar as folly and pride,
    Though dressed in red slippers and lace.

Not all the fine things that fine ladies possess
    Should teach them the poor to despise;
For 'tis in good manners, and not in good dress,
    That the truest gentility lies.

JANE AND ANN TAYLOR

89. THE PIN

Dear me! what signifies a pin!
    I'll leave it on the floor;
My pin-cushion has others in,
    Mamma has plenty more:
A miser will I never be,
Said little heedless Emily.

So tripping on to giddy play,
    She left the pin behind,
For Betty's broom to whisk away,
    Or someone else to find;
She never gave a thought, indeed,
To what she might to-morrow need.

Next day a party was to ride,
    To see an air-balloon!
And all the company beside
    Were dress'd and ready soon:
But she, poor girl, she could not stir,
For just a pin to finish her.

'Twas vainly now, with eye and hand,
    She did to search begin;
There was not one—not one, the band
    Of her pelisse to pin!
She cut her pin-cushion in two,
But not a pin had slidden through!

At last, as hunting on the floor,
    Over a crack she lay,
The carriage rattled to the door,
    Then rattled fast away.
Poor Emily! she was not in,
For want of just—a single pin!

There's hardly anything so small,
    So trifling or so mean,
That we may never want at all,
    For service unforeseen:
And those who venture wilful waste,
May woeful want expect to taste.

JANE TAYLOR

90. DREADFUL STORY ABOUT HARRIET
AND THE MATCHES

It almost makes me cry to tell
What foolish Harriet befell.
Mamma and nurse went out one day
And left her all alone at play;
Now, on the table close at hand,
A box of matches chanced to stand;
And kind Mamma and Nurse had told her,
That, if she touched them, they should scold her.
But Harriet said: 'Oh, what a pity!
For, when they burn, it is so pretty;
They crackle so, and spit, and flame;
Mamma, too, often does the same.'

The pussy cats heard this,
And they began to hiss,
And stretch their claws,
And raise their paws;
'Me-ow,' they said, 'me-ow, me-o,
You'll burn to death, if you do so.'

But Harriet would not take advice;
She lit a match, it was so nice!
It crackled so, it burned so clear—
Exactly like the picture here.
She jumped for joy and ran about,
And was too pleased to put it out.

The pussy-cats saw this
And said: 'Oh, naughty, naughty, Miss,'
And stretched their claws,
And raised their paws:

'Tis very, very wrong, you know,
Me-ow, me-o, me-ow, me-o,
You will be burnt, if you do so.'

And see! oh! what a dreadful thing!
The fire has caught her apron-string;
Her apron burns, her arms, her hair;
She burns all over, everywhere.

Then how the pussy-cats did mew—
What else, poor pussies, could they do?
They screamed for help, 'twas all in vain!
So then they said: 'We'll scream again,
Make haste, make haste, me-ow, me-o,
She'll burn to death, we told her so.'

So she was burnt, with all her clothes,
And arms, and hands, and eyes, and nose;
Till she had nothing more to lose
Except her little scarlet shoes;
And nothing else but these was found
Among her ashes on the ground.

And when the good cats sat beside
The smoking ashes, how they cried!
'Me-ow, me-oo, me-ow, me-oo;
What will Mamma and Nursey do?'
Their tears ran down their cheeks so fast,
They made a little pond at last.

HEINRICH HOFFMANN

91. RHYME

There was an old woman, as I've heard tell,
She went to market her eggs for to sell;
She went to market all on a market day;
And she fell asleep on the King's highway.

There came by a pedlar whose name was Stout,
He cut her petticoats all round about;
He cut her petticoats up to the knees,
Which made the old woman to shiver and freeze.

When this little woman first did wake,
She began to shiver and she began to shake.
She began to wonder and she began to cry,
'Lauk-a-mercy on me, this is none of I:

But if it be I, as I do hope it be,
I've a little dog at home, and he'll know me;
If it be I, he'll wag his little tail,
And if it be not I, he'll loudly bark and wail.'

Home went the little woman all in the dark,
Up got the little dog, and he began to bark;
He began to bark, so she began to cry,
'Lauk-a-mercy on me, this is none of I!'

92. JACK-OF-THE-INKPOT

I dance on your paper,
I hide in your pen,
I make in your ink-stand
My little black den;

And when you're not looking
I hop on your nose,
And leave on your forehead
The marks of my toes.

When you're trying to finish
Your 'i' with a dot,
I slip down your finger
And make it a blot;
And when you're so busy
To cross a big 'T',
I make on the paper
A little Black Sea.

I drink blotting-paper,
Eat penwiper pie,
You never can catch me,
You never need try!
I leap any distance,
I use any ink,
I'm on to your fingers
Before you can wink.

ALGERNON BLACKWOOD

93. THE SENTINELS

Up and down the nurs'ry stair
All through the night
There are Fairy Sentinels
Watching till it's light;
If they ever went to sleep
The Big Clock would tell;
But, Left, Right! Left—Right!
They know their duty well.

I needn't mind a Bogey or a Beetle or a Bear,
The Sentinels are watching—on the nurs'ry stair!

Up and down the nurs'ry stair
All through the day
There the Fairy Sentinels
Sleep the time away;
If you were to wake them up,
Think how tired they'd be,
So Tip-toe! Tip-toe!
Go upstairs quietly.
Yes, that's the very reason we have carpets on the
     stair,
The Sentinels are sleeping, and we must take care.

ETHEL TALBOT

94. THE FAIRY SHIP

I saw a ship a-sailing,
   A-sailing on the sea;
And oh! it was all laden
   With pretty things for thee!

There were comfits in the cabin,
   And apples in the hold;
The sails were made of silk,
   And the masts were made of gold.

The four and twenty sailors
   That stood between the decks,
Were four and twenty white mice,
   With chains about their necks.

The captain was a duck,
    With a jacket on his back;
And when the ship began to move
    The captain said 'Quack! quack!'

95. EARL HALDAN'S DAUGHTER

It was Earl Haldan's daughter,
She looked across the sea,
She looked across the water,
And long and loud laughed she.
'The locks of six princesses
Must be my marriage fee,
So hey, bonny boat, and ho, bonny boat,
Who comes a-wooing me?'

It was Earl Haldan's daughter,
She looked across the sand,
When she was aware of a knight so fair
Come sailing to the land.
His sails were all of velvet,
His mast of beaten gold,
'And hey, bonny boat, and ho, bonny boat,
Who saileth here so bold?'

'The locks of five princesses
I won beyond the sea,
I clipt their golden tresses
To fringe a cloak for thee;
One handful yet is wanting,
But one of all the tale,
So hey, bonny boat, and ho, bonny boat,
Furl up thy velvet sail.'

He leapt into the water,
That rover young and bold,
He gript Earl Haldan's daughter,
He clipt her locks of gold.
'Go weep, go weep, proud maiden,
The tale is full to-day.
Now hey, bonny boat, and ho, bonny boat,
Sail Westward ho, away.'

CHARLES KINGSLEY

96. THE CHILDREN'S SONG

The Wee Red-headed Man is a knowing sort of
    fellow,
His coat is cat's-eye green and his pantaloons are
    yellow.
His brogues are made of glass and his hose are red
    as cherry—
He's the lad for devilment, if you only make him
    merry.

He drives a flock of goats, has another flock behind
    him—
The little children fear him, but the old folk never
    mind him.
To the frogs' house and the goats' house and the
    hilly land and hollow,
He will carry naughty children where their parents
    dare not follow.

Oh! little ones, beware. If the Red-haired Man
    should catch you,
Rats will be your playmates and frogs and eels will
    watch you—

A bed between two rocks and not a fire to warm
    you!—
But, little ones, be good and the Red-haired Man
    can't harm you.

The Wee Red-headed Man has piles and piles of
    riches,
Guineas in his wallet and the pockets of his
    britches.
And if you're very poor and meet him, he is willing
To bargain for your soul, if you'll sell it for a
    shilling.

He's cute and he is coaxing and hard although he's
    civil—
But let him get your soul and he'll give it to the
    devil,
And when the devil gets it (the devil's hoof is
    cloven)
He'll spit it and he'll steam it and he'll roast it in an
    oven.

But, children, if the Red-Haired Man comes up to
    you, don't worry,
Just say, 'Excuse me, Sir, to-day, for I am in a
    hurry!'
He'll say, 'Be off!' Then shake your heels; let one
    leg race the other
And never turn to look behind, till you get home to
    mother!

PATRICK MACGILL

97. CRAB-APPLE

I dreamed the Fairies wanted me
   To spend my birth-night with them all;
And I said, 'Oh, but you're so wee
   And I am so tremendous tall,
What could we do?'
       'Crab-apple stem!'
Said they, and I was just like them.

And then, when we were all the same,
   The party and the fun began;
They said they'd teach me a new game
   Of 'Dew-Ponds'. 'I don't think I can
Play that,' I said.
       'Crab-apple blue!'
Said they, and I could play it too.

And then, when we had played and played,
   The Fairies said that we would dance;
And I said, 'Oh, but I'm afraid
   That I've no shoes.' I gave a glance
At my bare toes.
       'Crab-apple sweet!'
Said they, and shoes were on my feet.

And then we danced away, away,
   Until my birth-night all was done;
And I said, 'I'll go home to-day;
   And thank you for my lovely fun,
I'll come again.'
       'Crab-apple red!'
Said they, and I woke up in bed.

ETHEL TALBOT

98. VISION

I've seen her, I've seen her
Beneath an apple tree;
The minute that I saw her there
With stars and dewdrops in her hair,
I knew it must be she.
She's sitting on a dragon-fly
All shining green and gold,
A little way above the ground;
The dragon-fly goes circling round—
She isn't taking hold.

I've seen her, I've seen her—
I never, never knew
That anything could be so sweet;
She has the tiniest hands and feet,
Her wings are very blue.
She holds her little head like this
Because she is a queen;
(I can't describe it all in words)
She's throwing kisses to the birds
And laughing in between.

I've seen her, I've seen her—
I simply ran and ran;
Put down your sewing quickly, please,
Let's hurry to the orchard trees
As softly as we can.
I had to go and leave her there,
I felt I couldn't stay,—
I wanted you to see her too—
But, oh, whatever shall we do
If she has flown away?

ROSE FYLEMAN

99. THE FAIRIES

Up the airy mountain,
  Down the rushy glen,
We daren't go a-hunting
  For fear of little men;
Wee folk, good folk,
  Trooping all together;
Green jacket, red cap,
  And white owl's feather!

Down along the rocky shore
  Some make their home,
They live on crispy pancakes
  Of yellow tide-foam;
Some in the reeds
  Of the black mountain-lake,
With frogs for their watch-dogs,
  All night awake.

High on the hill-top
  The old King sits;
He is now so old and grey
  He's nigh lost his wits.
With a bridge of white mist
  Columbkill he crosses,
On his stately journeys
  From Slieveleague to Rosses;
Or going up with music
  On cold starry nights,
To sup with the Queen
  Of the gay Northern Lights.

They stole little Bridget
  For seven years long;

When she came down again
   Her friends were all gone.
They took her lightly back,
   Between the night and morrow;
They thought that she was fast asleep,
   But she was dead with sorrow.
They have kept her ever since
   Deep within the lake,
On a bed of flag-leaves,
   Watching till she wake.

By the craggy hill-side,
   Through the mosses bare,
They have planted thorn-trees
   For pleasure here and there.
Is any man so daring
   As to dig them up in spite,
He shall find their sharpest thorns
   In his bed at night.

Up the airy mountain,
   Down the rushy glen,
We daren't go a-hunting
   For fear of little men;
Wee folk, good folk,
   Trooping all together;
Green jacket, red cap,
   And white owl's feather!

WILLIAM ALLINGHAM

100. COME UNTO THESE YELLOW SANDS

Come unto these yellow sands,
  And then take hands:
Curtsied when you have, and kiss'd,—
  The wild waves whist,—
Foot it featly here and there;
  And, sweet sprites, the burthen bear.
    Hark, hark!
      Bow-wow.
    The watch dogs bark:
      Bow-wow.
Hark, hark! I hear
The strain of strutting Chanticleer
  Cry, Cock-a-diddle-dow!

WILLIAM SHAKESPEARE

101. PICNICS

If you go a-picnicking and throw your scraps about
You'll never see the little folk go running in and out,
And if you leave your orange-peel all littered on the
  grass
You'll never go to Fairy Land or see the fairies pass.
For empty tins and tangled strings
And paper bags are not the things
To scatter where a linnet sings.

So if you go a-picnicking remember you're a guest
Of all the tiny people, and you'll really find it best
To leave their ball-room tidy and to clear away the
  mess,
And *perhaps* you'll see a fairy in her newest dancing
  dress.

But paper bags and broken combs
Will really wreck the pixie homes
And frighten all the tiny gnomes.

But if you go a-picnicking and you are elfin-wise
You'll maybe hear with fairy ears and see with
     goblin eyes;
The little folk will welcome you and they will open
     wide
The hidden doors of Fairy Land, and you will pass
     inside,
And maybe see a baby fay
White cradled in a cherry spray
Although it is Bank Holiday.

B. E. TODD

102. RILLOBY-RILL

Grasshoppers four a-fiddling went,
    Heigh-ho! never be still!
They earned but little towards their rent
But all day long with their elbows bent
    They fiddled a tune called Rilloby-rilloby,
    Fiddled a tune called Rilloby-rill.

Grasshoppers soon on Fairies came,
    Heigh-ho! never be still!
Fairies asked with a manner of blame,
'Where do you come from, what is your name,
    What do you want with your Rilloby-rilloby,
    What do you want with your Rilloby-rill?'

'Madam, you see before you stand,
    Heigh-ho! never be still!
The Old Original Favourite Grand

Grasshoppers' Green Herbarian Band,
   And the tune we play is Rilloby-rilloby,
   Madam, the tune is Rilloby-rill.'

Fairies hadn't a word to say,
   Heigh-ho! never be still!
Fairies seldom are sweet by day,
But the Grasshoppers merrily fiddled away,
   Oh, but they played with a willoby-rilloby,
   Oh, but they played with a willoby-will!

Fairies slumber and sulk at noon,
   Heigh-ho! never be still!
But at last the kind old motherly moon
Brought them dew in a silver spoon,
   And they turned to ask for Rilloby-rilloby,
   One more round of Rilloby-rill.

Ah, but nobody now replied,
   Heigh-ho! never be still!
When day went down the music died,
Grasshoppers four lay side by side.
   And there was an end of their Rilloby-rilloby,
   There was an end of their Rilloby-rill.

HENRY NEWBOLT

103. THE SEVEN FIDDLERS

A blue robe on their shoulder,
   And an ivory bow in hand,
Seven fiddlers came with their fiddles
   A-fiddling through the land,
And they fiddled a tune on their fiddles
   That none could understand.

For none who heard their fiddling
    Might keep his ten toes still,
E'en the cripple threw down his crutches,
    And danced against his will;
Young and old they all fell a-dancing,
    While the fiddlers fiddled their fill.

They fiddled down to the ferry—
    The ferry by Severn-side,
And they stept aboard the ferry,
    None else to row or guide,
And deftly steered the pilot,
    And stoutly the oars they plied.

Then suddenly in the mid-channel
    These fiddlers ceased to row,
And the pilot spake to his fellows
    In a tongue that none may know;
'Let us home to our father and brothers,
    And the maidens we love below.'

Then the fiddlers seized their fiddles,
    And sang to their fiddles a song;
'We are coming, coming, oh brothers,
    To the home we have left so long,
For the world still loves the fiddler,
    And the fiddler's tune is strong.'

Then they stept from out the ferry
    Into the Severn sea,
Down into the depths of the waters
    Where the homes of the fiddlers be,
And the ferry boat drifted slowly
    Forth to the ocean free!

But where those jolly fiddlers
  Walked down into the deep,
The ripples are never quiet,
  But for ever dance and leap,
Though the Severn sea be silent;
  And the winds be all asleep.

SEBASTIAN EVANS

104. FAIRY WORKERS

Said the Fairies of Kilfinnan
To the Fairies of Macroom:
'Oh! send to us a shuttle
For our little fairy loom,
Our workers, one and twenty
Are waiting in the coom—'
So Kilfinnan got a shuttle
From the Fairies of Macroom.

Kilfinnan got the shuttle,
The shuttle for the loom.
'Now send us back a hammer,'
Said the Fairies of Macroom.
'We've cobblers, one and twenty,
All idle in their room.'
And Kilfinnan sent a hammer
To the Fairies of Macroom.

The Queen of all the Fairies
Sat in her drawing-room:
Her robes came from Kilfinnan
Her brogues came from Macroom.

Now, at the Royal Dinner
The proudest in the room
Were the Fairies from Kilfinnan
And the Fairies from Macroom.

PATRICK MACGILL

105. THE FAIRY QUEEN

Come follow, follow me,
You, fairy elves that be:
Which circle on the green,
Come follow Mab, your queen.
Hand in hand let's dance around,
For this place is fairy ground.

When mortals are at rest,
And snoring in their nest;
Unheard and unespied,
Through keyholes we do glide;
Over tables, stools and shelves,
We trip it with our fairy elves.

And if the house be foul
With platter, dish or bowl,
Upstairs we nimbly creep,
And find the sluts asleep:
There we pinch their arms and thighs:
None escapes, nor none espies.

But if the house be swept,
And from uncleanness kept,
We praise the household maid,
And duly she is paid:
For we use before we go
To drop a tester in her shoe.

106

Upon a mushroom's head
Our tablecloth we spread;
A grain of rye, or wheat,
Is manchet, which we eat;
Pearly drops of dew we drink
In acorn-cups filled to the brink.

The grasshopper, gnat, and fly
Serve for our minstrelsy;
Grace said, we dance awhile,
And so the time beguile;
And if the moon doth hide her head;
The glow-worm lights us home to bed.

On tops of dewy grass
So nimbly do we pass,
The young and tender stalk
Ne'er bends when we do walk;
Yet in the morning may be seen
Where we the night before have been.

106. FAIRIES

There are fairies at the bottom of our garden!
   It's not so very, very far away;
You pass the gardener's shed and you just keep
      straight ahead—
   I do so hope they've really come to stay.
There's a little wood, with moss in it and beetles,
   And a little stream that quietly runs through;
You wouldn't think they'd dare to come merry-
      making there—
      Well, they do.

There are fairies at the bottom of our garden!
　　They often have a dance on summer nights;
The butterflies and bees make a lovely little breeze,
　　And the rabbits stand about and hold the lights.
Did you know that they could sit upon the moon-
　　　　beams
　　And pick a little star to make a fan,
And dance away up there in the middle of the air?
　　　　Well, they can.

There are fairies at the bottom of our garden!
　　You cannot think how beautiful they are;
They all stand up and sing when the Fairy Queen
　　　　and King
　　Come gently floating down upon their car.
The King is very proud and *very* handsome;
　　The Queen—now can you guess who that could
　　　　be
(She's a little girl all day, but at night she steals
　　　　away)?
　　　　　　Well—it's ME!

ROSE FYLEMAN

107. THE FAIRY LIFE

Where the bee sucks, there suck I
In a cowslip's bell I lie;
There I couch when owls do cry.
On the bat's back I do fly
After summer merrily:
　　Merrily, merrily shall I live now
　　Under the blossom that hangs on the bough!

WILLIAM SHAKESPEARE

108. MELMILLO

Three and thirty birds there stood
In an elder in a wood;
Called Melmillo—flew off three,
Leaving thirty in the tree;
Called Melmillo—nine now gone,
And the boughs held twenty-one;
Called Melmillo—and eighteen
Left but three to nod and preen;
Called Melmillo—three—two—one—
Now of birds were feathers none.

Then stole slim Melmillo in
To that wood all dusk and green,
And with lean long palms outspread
Softly a strange dance did tread;
Not a note of music she
Had for echoing company;
All the birds were flown to rest
In the hollow of her breast;
In the wood—thorn, elder, willow—
Dance alone—lone danced Melmillo.

WALTER DE LA MARE

109. SING ME A SONG

Sing me a song.—
    What shall I sing?—
Three merry sisters
    Dancing in a ring,
Light and fleet upon their feet
    As birds upon the wing.

Tell me a tale.—
  What shall I tell?—
Two mournful sisters,
  And a tolling knell,
Tolling ding and tolling dong,
  Ding dong bell.

CHRISTINA ROSSETTI

110. THE BALLAD OF SEMMERWATER

Deep asleep, deep asleep,
Deep asleep it lies,
The still lake of Semmerwater
Under the still skies.

And many a fathom, many a fathom,
Many a fathom below,
In a king's tower and a queen's bower
The fishes come and go.

Once there stood by Semmerwater
A mickle tower and tall;
King's tower and queen's bower,
And the wakeman on the wall.

Came a beggar halt and sore:
'I faint for lack of bread.'
King's tower and queen's bower
Cast him forth unfed.

He knocked at the door of the eller's cot,
The eller's cot in the dale.
They gave him of their oatcake,
They gave him of their ale.

He has cursed aloud that city proud,
He has cursed it in its pride;
He has cursed it into Semmerwater
Down the brant hillside;
He has cursed it into Semmerwater,
There to bide.

King's tower and queen's bower,
And a mickle town and tall;
By glimmer of scale and gleam of fin,
Folk have seen them all.
King's tower and queen's bower,
And weed and reed in the gloom;
And a lost city in Semmerwater,
Deep asleep till Doom.

WILLIAM WATSON

III. AS LUCY WENT A-WALKING

As Lucy went a-walking one morning cold and fine
There sat three crows upon a bough, and three
    times three is nine:
Then 'Oh!' said Lucy in the snow, 'it's very plain
    to see
A witch has been a-walking in the field in front of
    me.'

Then stept she light and heedfully across the frozen
    snow,
And plucked a bunch of elder twigs that near a pool
    did grow:
And, by and by, she comes to seven shadows in one
    place
Stretched black by seven poplar trees against the
    sun's bright face.

She looks to left, she looks to right, and in the
  midst she sees
A little pool of water clear and frozen 'neath the
  trees;
Then down beside its margent in the crusty snow
  she kneels,
And hears a magic belfry a-ringing with sweet bells.

Clear sang the faint far merry peal, then silence on
  the air,
And icy-still the frozen pool and poplars standing
  there:
Then lo! as Lucy turned her head and looked along
  the snow
She sees a witch—a witch she sees, come frisking to
  and fro.

Her scarlet buckled shoes they clicked, her heels
  a-twinkling high,
With mistletoe her steepled hat bobbed as she
  capered by;
But never a dint, or mark, or print, in the whiteness
  for to see
Though danced she high, though danced she fast,
  though danced she lissomely.

It seemed 'twas diamonds in the air, or little flakes
  of frost;
It seemed 'twas golden smoke around, or sunbeams
  lightly tossed;
It seemed an elfin music like to reeds and warblers
  rose;
'Nay,' Lucy said, 'it is the wind that through the
  branches flows.'

And as she peeps, and as she peeps, 'tis no one
      more but three,
And eye of bat, and downy wing of owl within the
      tree,
And the bells of that sweet belfry a-pealing as
      before,
And now it is not three she sees, and now it is not
      four.

'O! who are ye,' sweet Lucy cries, 'that in a
      dreadful ring
All muffled up in brindled shawls, do caper, frisk
      and spring?'
'A witch, and witches, one and nine,' they straight
      to her reply,
And looked upon her narrowly, with green and
      needling eye.

Then Lucy sees in clouds of gold green cherry trees
      upgrow
And bushes of red roses that bloomed above the
      snow;
She smells, all faint, the almond boughs blowing so
      wild and fair,
And doves with milky eyes ascend fluttering in the
      air.

Clear flowers she sees, like tulip buds, go floating
      by like birds,
With wavering tips that warbled sweetly strange
      enchanted words;
And, as with ropes of amethyst, the boughs with
      lamps were hung,
And clusters of green emeralds like fruit upon
      them clung.

O, witches nine, ye dreadful nine, O, witches seven
and three!
Whence come these wondrous things that I this
Christmas morning see?'
But straight, as in a clap, when she of *Christmas*
says the word—
Here is the snow, and there the sun, but never
bloom nor bird;
Nor warbling flame, nor gloaming rope of amethyst
there shows,
Nor bunches of green emeralds, nor belfry, well,
and rose,
Nor cloud of gold, nor cherry tree, nor witch in
brindled shawl,
But like a dream that vanishes so vanished were
they all.

When Lucy sees and sees alone three crows upon a
bough,
And earthly twigs, and bushes hidden white in
driven snow,
Then 'Oh,' said Lucy, 'three times three is nine—I
plainly see
Some witch has been a-walking in the fields in front
of me.'

WALTER DE LA MARE

112. THE NIX

The crafty Nix, more false than fair
    Whose haunt in arrowy Iser lies,
She envied me my golden hair,
    She envied me my azure eyes.

114

The moon with silvery ciphers traced
    The leaves, and on the waters play'd;
She rose, she caught me round the waist,
    She said, 'Come down with me, fair maid.'

She led me to her crystal grot,
    She set me in her coral chair,
She waved her hand, and I had not
    Or azure eyes or golden hair.

Her locks of jet, her eyes of flame
    Were mine, and hers my semblance fair;
'O make me, Nix, again the same,
    O give me back my golden hair!'

She smiles in scorn, she disappears,
    And here I sit and see no sun,
My eyes of fire are quenched in tears,
    And all my darksome locks undone.

RICHARD GARNETT

113. TRUE THOMAS

True Thomas lay on yon grassy bank,
    And he beheld a lady gay,
A lady that was blithe and bold,
    Come riding o'er the ferny brae.

Her skirt was of the grass-green silk,
    Her mantle of the velvet fine,
At each lock of her horse's mane
    Hung fifty silver bells and nine.

True Thomas, he took off his hat,
   And bowed him low down to his knee;
'All hail, thou mighty Queen of Heaven!
   For thy like on earth I ne'er did see.'

'Oh no, oh no, True Thomas,' she says,
   'That name does not belong to me;
I am but the Queen of fair Elfland,
   And I'm come here to visit thee.

'But ye must go with me, Thomas,
   True Thomas, ye must go with me,
For ye must serve me seven years,
   Through weal or woe, as chance may be.'

She turned upon her milk-white steed,
   And took True Thomas up behind,
And aye whene'er her bridle rang,
   The steed flew swifter than the wind.

For forty days and forty nights
   He rode through bracken to the knee,
And he saw neither sun nor moon,
   But heard the roaring of the sea.

'Oh, see ye not that bonny road
   Which winds about the ferny brake?
That is the road to fair Elfland,
   Which thou and I this night must take.

'But Thomas, ye must hold your tongue,
   Whatever ye may hear or see,
For if one word ye should chance to speak,
   Ye'll ne'er get back to your own country.'

He has gotten a coat of the elfin cloth,
　And a pair of shoes of velvet green;
And till seven years were past and gone,
　True Thomas on earth was never seen.

OLD BALLAD

II4. THE BABES IN THE WOOD

Now ponder well, you parents dear,
These words which I shall write;
A doleful story you shall hear,
In time brought forth to light.
A gentleman of good account
In Norfolk dwelt of late,
Who did in honour far surmount
Most men of his estate.

Sore sick he was and like to die,
No help his life could save;
His wife by him as sick did lie,
And both possessed one grave.
No love between these two was lost,
Each was to other kind;
In love they lived, in love they died,
And left two babes behind.

The one a fine and pretty boy,
Not passing three years old;
The other, a girl more young than he,
And framed in beauty's mould.
The father left his little son,
As plainly did appear,
When he to perfect age should come,
Three hundred pounds a year.

And to his little daughter Jane,
Five hundred pounds in gold,
To be paid down on marriage-day,
Which might not be controlled:
But if the children chanced to die
Ere they to age should come,
Their uncle should possess their wealth;
For so the will did run.

'Now, brother,' said the dying man,
'Look to my children dear;
Be good unto my boy and girl,
No friends else have they here;
To God and you I recommend
My children dear this day;
But little while, be sure, we have
Within this world to stay.

'You must be father and mother both,
And uncle, all in one;
God knows what will become of them,
When I am dead and gone.'
With that bespake their mother dear:
'O brother kind,' quoth she,
'You are the man must bring our babes
To wealth or misery!

'And if you keep them carefully,
Then God will you reward;
But if you otherwise should deal,
God will your deeds regard.'
With lips as cold as any stone
They kissed their children small;
'God bless you both, my children dear!
With that the tears did fall.

These speeches then their brother spake
To this sick couple there;
'The keeping of your little ones,
Sweet sister, do not fear;
God never prosper me nor mine,
Nor aught else that I have,
If I do wrong your children dear,
When you are laid in grave.'

PART II

The parents being dead and gone,
The children home he takes,
And brings them straight unto his house,
Where much of them he makes.
He had not kept these pretty babes
A twelvemonth and a day,
But, for their wealth, he did devise
To make them both away.

He bargained with two ruffians strong,
Which were of furious mood,
That they should take these children young,
And slay them in a wood.
He told his wife an artful tale:
He would the children send,
To be brought up in London town
With one that was his friend.

Away then went those pretty babes,
Rejoicing at that tide,
Rejoicing in a merry mind,
They should on cock-horse ride.

They prate and prattle pleasantly
As they rode on the way
To those that should their butchers be,
And take their lives' decay.

So that the pretty speech they had
Made Murder's heart relent;
And they that undertook the deed
Full sore did now repent.
Yet one of them, more hard of heart,
Did vow to do his charge,
Because the wretch that hirèd him
Had paid him very large.

The other won't agree thereto,
So here they fall to strife;
With one another they did fight
About the children's life:
And he that was of mildest mood
Did slay the other there,
Within an unfrequented wood;—
The babes did quake for fear!

He took the children by the hand,
Tears standing in their eye,
And bade them straightway follow him,
And look they did not cry;
And two long miles he led them on,
While they for food complain:
'Stay here,' quoth he, 'I'll bring you bread,
When I come back again.'

These pretty babes, with hand in hand,
Went wandering up and down;
But never more could see the man
Approaching from the town.

Their pretty lips with blackberries
Were all besmeared and dyed;
And when they saw the darksome night,
They sat them down and cried.

Thus wandered these poor innocents,
Till death did end their grief;
In one another's arms they died
As wanting due relief:
No burial this pretty pair
From any man receives,
Till Robin Redbreast piously
Did cover them with leaves.

OLD BALLAD

115. THE FUGITIVES

I

The waters are flashing,
The white hail is dashing,
The lightnings are glancing,
The hoar-spray is dancing—
     Away!

The whirlwind is rolling,
The thunder is tolling,
The forest is swinging,
The minster bells ringing—
     Come away!

The earth is like ocean,
Wreck-strewn and in motion:
Bird, beast, man and worm
Have crept out of the storm—
     Come away!

II

'Our boat has one sail,
And the helmsman is pale;—
A bold pilot I trow,
Who shall follow us now,'—
　　　Shouted he—

And she cried: 'Ply the oar!
Put off gaily from shore!'—
As she spoke, bolts of death
Mixed with hail, specked their path
　　　　O'er the sea.

And from isle, tower and rock,
The blue beacon-cloud broke,
And though dumb in the blast,
The red cannon flashed fast
　　　From the lee.

And 'Fear'st thou?' and 'Fear'st thou?'
And 'See'st thou?' and 'Hear'st thou?'
And 'Drive we not free
O'er the terrible sea,
　　　I and thou?'

One boat-cloak did cover
The loved and the lover—
Their blood beats one measure,
They murmur proud pleasure
　　　Soft and low;—

While around the lashed ocean,
Like mountains in motion,
Is withdrawn and uplifted,
Sunk, shattered and shifted
     To and fro.

IV

In the court of the fortress
Beside the pale portress,
Like a bloodhound well beaten
The bridegroom stands, eaten
     By shame;

On the topmost watch-turret,
As a death-boding spirit,
Stands the grey tyrant father,
To his voice the mad weather
     Seems tame;

And with curses as wild
As e'er clung to child,
He devotes to the blast
The best, loveliest, and last
     Of his name!

PERCY BYSSHE SHELLEY

116. SLEEPING BEAUTY

The scent of bramble fills the air,
   Amid her folded sheets she lies,
The gold of evening in her hair,
   The blue of morn shut in her eyes.

How many a changing moon hath lit
  The unchanging roses of her face!
Her mirror ever broods on it
  In silver stillness of the days.

Oft flits the moth on filmy wings
  Into his solitary lair;
Shrill evensong the cricket sings
  From some still shadows in her hair.

In heat, in snow, in wind, in flood,
  She sleeps in lovely loneliness,
Half folded like an April bud
  On winter-haunted trees.

WALTER DE LA MARE

117. DAWN

The strange blue light which comes before the
    morn
Steals all along the marshy banks forlorn;

The noises of the night have died away,
There comes the hush that heralds in the day,
  The boat is floating down to Camelot.

A wind sobs low and drifts among the sedge,
A primrose glow lifts the horizon's edge;

The river laps upon the barge's side,
Bearing it ever downward with the tide,
  The boat is floating down to Camelot.

The trees each side the river bend their head
In tender homage to the silent Dead.

And so between the hours of night and day,
The Lily-Maid passed down the river way,
  The boat has floated down to Camelot.

ALIX EGERTON

118. THE BALLAD OF SIR BORS

Would I could win some quiet and rest, and a little
    ease,
In the cool grey hush of the dusk, in the dim green
    place of the trees,
Where the birds are singing, singing, singing,
    crying aloud
The song of the red, red rose that blossoms beyond
    the seas.

Would I could see it, the rose, when the light begins
    to fail,
And a lone white star in the West is glimmering on
    the mail;
The red, red passionate rose of the sacred blood of
    the Christ,
In the shining chalice of God, the cup of the Holy
    Grail.

The dusk comes gathering grey, and the darkness
    dims the West,
The oxen low to the byre, and all bells ring to rest;
But I ride over the moors, for the dusk still bides
    and waits,
That brims my soul with the glow of the rose that
    ends the Quest.

My horse is spavined and ribbed, and his bones
    come through his hide,
My sword is rotten with rust, but I shake the reins
    and ride,
For the bright white birds of God that nest in the
    rose have called,
And never a township now is a town where I can
    bide.

It will happen at last, at dusk, as my horse limps
    down the fell,
A star will glow like a note God strikes on a silver
    bell,
And the bright white birds of God will carry my
    soul to Christ,
And the sight of the Rose, the Rose, will pay for the
    years of hell.

JOHN MASEFIELD

119. HEAVEN

O who will show me those delights on high?
                ECHO: *I.*
Thou, Echo, thou art mortal, all men know.
                ECHO: *No.*
Wert thou not born among the trees and leaves?
                ECHO: *Leaves.*
And are there any leaves that still abide?
                ECHO: *Bide.*
What leaves are they? impart the matter wholly.
                ECHO: *Holy.*
Are holy leaves the Echo, then, of bliss?
                ECHO: *Yes.*

Then tell me, what is that supreme delight?
>Echo: *Light*.

Light to the mind: what shall the will enjoy?
>Echo: *Joy*.

But are there cares and business with the pleasure?
>Echo: *Leisure*.

Light, joy and leisure; but shall they persever?
>Echo: *Ever*.

GEORGE HERBERT

I2O. GOD SAVE THE KING

God save our gracious King,
Nation and State and King,
>God save the King!
Grant him the Peace divine,
But if his Wars be Thine
Flash on our fighting line
>Victory's Wing!

Thou in his suppliant hands
Hast placed such Mighty Lands:
>Save Thou our King!
As once from golden Skies
Rebels with flaming eyes,
So the King's Enemies
>Doom Thou and fling!

Mountains that break the night
Holds he by eagle right
>Stretching far Wing!

127

Dawn lands for Youth to reap,
Dim lands where Empires sleep,
His! And the Lion Deep
     Roars for the King.

But most these few dear miles
Of sweetly-meadowed Isles,—
     England all Spring;
Scotland that by the marge
Where the blank North doth charge
Hears Thy Voice loud and large,
     Save, and their King!

Grace on the golden Dales
Of Thine old Christian Wales
     Shower till they sing,
Till Erin's Island lawn
Echoes the dulcet-drawn
Song with a cry of Dawn—
     God save the King!

       JAMES ELROY FLECKER

INDEX OF TITLES

I

INDEX OF FIRST LINES

136